VOLUME 18

FUNK & WAGNALLS WILDLIFE ENCYCLOPEDIA

GENERAL EDITORS • Dr. Maurice Burton and Robert Burton

Also published as The International Wildlife Encyclopedia and Encyclopedia of Animal Life.
Funk & Wagnalls, Inc., New York, New York

Skylark

Larks are famous for their songs, but none is so well known as the skylark, which has inspired poets, particularly Shelley, who referred to it as 'blithe spirit'. While the song is familiar to all of us the skylark itself is often overlooked. It is a drab brown bird, about 7 in. long. The plumage is brown streaked with black on the upper parts and breast and whitish underneath. It could easily be dismissed as just another small, brown bird if it were not for the white feathers edging the tail and the short crest. The latter is much less conspicuous than that of some other larks such as the crested lark (p 567).

Sometimes it appears as if a skylark has no more than a ruffled head and often the crest is laid flat so that it cannot be seen.

Skylarks breed in most of Europe, except the extreme north of Scandinavia, in North Africa and across Asia to Japan and the Bering Straits. Because of the popularity of its song the skylark has been introduced to many other parts of the world, such as New Zealand, Hawaii and Vancouver Island off the west coast of Canada.

Lives in open country

Over most of Europe and North Africa the range of the skylark overlaps that of the woodlark. The latter is a little smaller and has conspicuous white eye-stripes. The song is different from that of a skylark and dur-ing the nesting season the woodlark is found on the edges of woods or among scattered trees. The skylark, which is known as the fieldlark in other languages, is typi-cally found in pastures, moors and marshes, but not near trees.

In the autumn skylarks migrate south in flocks, but to the casual observer it may appear as if there has been no migration at all because skylarks, in temperate Europe at least, are as common in winter as they are in summer. This is because there has been a sort of 'General Post'. Shortly after breed-ing, as skylarks fly south, more skylarks arrive from the north to take their place, some just passing through but others stay-ing for the winter. In the British Isles, the native skylarks leave in September—Novem-ber, and during this time they are replaced

▽ *Just another small brown bird? White feathers on the edge of its tail identify this skylark, or fieldlark, as it takes a drink.*

by immigrants from northern and central Europe. Those from the north stay, living in flocks, while those from central Europe continue their journey southwards.

Mixed diet

Skylarks feed on a mixture of animal and vegetable food. Over half their food is plants, particularly seeds of corn, chickweed, and the leaves of clover. They also eat a variety of small animals, such as earthworms, insects, millipedes and spiders.

Long-playing song

The song of the skylark can be heard nearly all the year round; even the winter visitors sing, and skylarks also sing while on migration. The song itself hardly needs description; it is a clear rather tuneless warble that may continue unbroken for up to 5 minutes, which poses the problem of how the skylark can breathe at the same time. The song is delivered during a song flight, similar to that of the pipits (p 1776). The skylark flies up vertically, starting to sing almost as soon as it clears the ground. The song continues until the skylark is little more than a speck in the sky poised on fluttering wings. It then sinks as gradually as it ascended and

finally drops to the ground and disappears in the grass. The song is sometimes delivered from a post or from the ground.

The small nest, 2½ in. across, is always built on the ground, usually among grass where it is very difficult to find because it is made of grass stems and is hidden by stems that form a tangle over it. There is, however, a 'pathway' leading through the grass to the nest and sometimes a skylark can be seen landing and running to its nest. There are usually 3 or 4 eggs in a clutch, greenish-white with brown speckles. They are incubated by the female alone for 11 days. The young are fed by both parents, and leave the nest when just over 1 week old but do not fly for 3 weeks.

Almost always singing

The skylark is one of the few birds that sings almost all the year round. Other European birds that do so include the wren, the robin and the song thrush. The time spent singing depends on a variety of circumstances but seems to have neither rhyme nor reason. For example, the male's singing reaches a peak in March or April—understandable because he is then holding a territory and

courting. It becomes relatively infrequent during nest-building and incubation, although he does not take part in these activities, and there is no obvious reason why he should not be singing. Then he sings again while the chicks are being fed even though he helps in the feeding. The one thing that does seem to upset a skylark's song is fog or very high winds. Skylarks sing less under these weather conditions although some of them still continue to sing from the ground.

class	**Aves**
order	**Passeriformes**
family	**Alaudidae**
genus & species	*Alauda arvensis*

▽ *Grass roots beginnings: three skylark chicks nestle in their cup-shaped nest of woven grass stems, well hidden in the undergrowth. The chicks are fed by both parents. They land on the ground some distance from the nest and reach it by a tiny pathway through the grass.*

Slater

Strictly speaking the name 'slater' is an alternative for woodlouse, but it tends to be applied more to a species related to wood- lice living by the sea. Woodlice will be described separately, but the sea-slater merits special treatment not so much for its unusual size — up to 1½ in. in males and 2 in. in females — but for its half terrestrial, half marine way of life. Sea-slaters are drably coloured, blackish, dark greyish green or light dirty brown. There are seven segments to the thorax, the fourth being the widest part of the roughly oval body. Behind the thorax is an abdomen of five segments with respiratory lobes on its appendages ending in a telson bearing two pairs of sensory 'tails'. On the head are two large black compound eyes, unstalked, and two pairs of antennae, the first minute and the second very long.

▽ *Speedy peabugs: at 16 steps per second per leg, slaters — these are **Ligia oceanica** — reach a frantic 1 mph, nearly an arthropod record.*

Slippery slaters

The sea-slater *Ligia oceanica* lives on the coasts of Europe and North America, and there are several other species on the Euro- pean and American coasts. Other species are found on coasts throughout the world. Although they do sometimes venture farther down the beach, sea-slaters live mostly just above high-tide level, hiding by day in cracks and crevices so that their abundance is not often appreciated. They are not found far inland, only within the zone splashed by sea spray — though in some places, as on the island of St Kilda, with steep cliffs, this can extend 450 ft up. Slaters also occur up the sides of estuaries and in salt marshes. Their abundance on quays has earned them the alternative names of quay-lice or quay- lowders. At certain times on the rocky shores of Japan slaters are so abundant that fishermen sweep them up with brooms for bait. Slaters are very fast runners, each leg making over sixteen steps per second, this rate being equalled by few other arthropods. With a step of about ⅜ in., a large slater scuttles at just over 1 mph, a very fast rate for so small an animal. Slaters are very much creatures of darkness, even moon- light is enough to keep them hidden.

Sweating in the sun

On a dark night, when the tide is out, they descend the shore to feed. They are par- ticularly fond of bladderwrack and other seaweeds, but they are general scavengers of organic matter and in captivity, at least, they may eat each other. As they hunt at night, they avoid being preyed upon by birds but many are caught by crabs. Drying up is another problem, for they readily lose water by evaporation through their cuticle. Nevertheless, they are fairly tolerant of water loss, their large size helps in this respect, and can sometimes turn evapora- tion to advantage in combating yet another problem — that of overheating as the sun beats down on the shore. It has been found that in dry air, when evaporation from the body is critical, the internal temperature of a slater may be as much as 7 C below that of the surrounding air. The slater is then losing heat by evaporation just as we do when we sweat. Because of this it some- times pays a slater to move out from under a stone and into sunlight where more eva- poration can take place. Water loss is made good by drinking — though, as in other isopods, drinking is more often through the anus than through the mouth.

Jane Burton: Photo Res

The widespread species *L. oceanica* may be found covered by the tide and has been known to survive months in seawater in the laboratory and to fast during this time. It has also survived 1½–8 days in distilled water. Several species, for example, *L. baudiensis* of Bermuda, which follows the ebbing tide and retreats as the sun dries the beach, cannot stand long immersion and, if pursued, only enter the water if there is no other escape route.

Young born in a pouch

The mature female has a thin plate on each of the first five pairs of legs that curves down and inwards and overlaps the opposite and adjacent plates. Together they make up a brood chamber. The male fertilises the eggs after they are laid in this, using a pair of grooved and two-jointed styles on his second pair of abdominal appendages to insert sperm into the brood chamber. After the eggs have hatched a brood of about 80 young are sheltered in the pouch and then released into the sea looking like miniatures of their parents. Females with broods can be found throughout the year, but especially in spring. In warmer parts of the world more especially there can occur 'plagues' of slaters. When this happens they often invade houses near quays and wharfs.

As in other crustaceans, growth in slaters involves periodic casting of the skin. Some days before a moult, the underneath of the first four segments of the thorax begins to develop a chalky whiteness. The upper surface of these segments also becomes lighter in colour. The old skin then splits behind these segments and the hind portion is shed. The front part is not cast until about 4 days later. As a result of this two-stage moult, one often finds individuals with the hind end lighter than the front. The change in size after moulting is not very obvious. As near as one can estimate, sea-slaters probably live about 3 years.

Rhythmic colour change

With their drab colours sea-slaters tend to merge with their surroundings even when not actually hidden away. Their ability to do this is helped by a tendency to grow lighter or darker according to the darkness of the background, by the contraction or expansion of their chromatophores. The stimulus to do this is through the eyes; a blind slater does not respond to a change in background. There is, however, another response that occurs even if the slater is blind: a blanching in darkness and a darkening in the light. These responses involve two hormones with opposing actions on the colour. In some species of *Ligia* there is a rhythmic lightening and darkening that continues even in constant darkness, the lightest colour being attained around midnight and the darkest in the morning.

△ *Slater **Nerocila bivittata** on the tail of a wrasse. Most slaters feed on plants in the sea shore splash zone, but species of this genus use sharp prehensile legs to cling to the fins, sometimes the bodies, of fishes, and through incisions made with adapted mouth parts, they suck the body fluids.*

GS Giacomelli

phylum	**Arthropoda**
class	**Crustacea**
order	**Isopoda**
genera	***Idotea, Ligia, Ligyda**, others*

Sloth

Sloths are bizarre mammals that spend nearly all their lives hanging upside down. With the anteaters and armadillos, these three South American groups belong to the order Edentata which means without teeth. The anteaters are the only edentates wholly without teeth but sloths have teeth in the cheeks. There are nine on each side and they grow throughout life. Their bodies show some remarkable adaptations for an upside down life in the trees. Sloths hang by means of long curved claws like meat hooks and their hands and feet have lost all other functions, the fingers and toes being united in a common fold of skin. The arms are longer than the legs and the pelvis is small. The back muscles which are well developed in other animals are weak in sloths. The head can turn through 270° so that it can be held almost the right way up while the rest of the body is upside down. The hair lies in the opposite direction to that of other mammals, from belly to back, so rain water still runs off it. The individual hairs are grooved and are usually infested by single-celled algae which make sloths look green.

The seven species of sloth are divided into two-toed and three-toed sloths. The three-toed sloths are about 2 ft long with a short stump-like tail. The two-toed sloths are a little larger but lack a tail. Sloths live in forests, the three-toed sloths from Honduras to northern Argentina and two-toed sloths from Venezuela to Brazil.

Slow-motion animals

As is usual for nocturnal animals living in the forests of South America, very little is known about their habits. Indeed sloths appear to have very few habits for they live in slow motion. Their movements along the branches are so slow that it is often said that a sloth may spend all its life on one tree. They eat, sleep, mate, give birth and nurse their young upside down, although they do not hang from branches all the time, as they will sit in the fork of a tree. They sleep with the head on the chest between the arms, looking very inconspicuous.

Sloths occasionally come to the ground, presumably to reach another tree when they cannot travel overhead by branches and creepers. They are just able to stand on their feet but they cannot walk on them. They move by sprawling on their bellies and dragging themselves forward with their hands. They can, however, swim well.

Despite their sluggish habits sloths can defend themselves well by slashing with their claws and by biting. It is often suggested that this is sufficient defence against their main enemies, jaguars and ocelots, but it is difficult to imagine a nimble cat being unable to outmanoeuvre a sloth. The sloths may benefit more as regards their enemies, from their camouflage of green algae and their sluggish habits which often make them look like a mass of dead leaves.

Popperfoto

△ *Just hanging around: a two-toed sloth picks its leisurely path through the tree canopy. All but a small fraction of a sloth's life is spent upside down; it eats, sleeps, mates and gives birth in this position, relying on formidable claws and a close resemblance to a bundle of leaves for defence.*

AR Devez: Jacana

△ *Earthbound ignominy: ill-adapted for anything but hanging, a three-toed sloth heaves and grovels its way to the next tree.*

▷ *Overleaf: Like mother, like child: a female three-toed sloth and young. A single baby is born at the start of the dry season.*

Plant eaters

Sloths eat mainly leaves and shoots with some fruit, which they may hook towards their mouths with their claws. Their stomachs are complex like those of ruminants such as cattle and sheep.

One baby

A single baby is born at the beginning of the dry season after a gestation of 17—26 weeks. It immediately hooks itself into the fur of its mother's breast and stays there until old enough to leave. Sloths have lived for 11 years in captivity.

Strange lodger

If a crop of green algae is not enough, sloth's fur harbours another guest—a moth rather like a clothes moth. The three species of pyralid moth have been found on the two species of sloth. They are about $\frac{1}{3}$ in. long with flattened bodies and can run agilely through the dense mat of hair. This makes them difficult to collect, especially as the collector has to avoid the sloth's attempts to defend itself. No one has been able to find out why the moths live in sloths' hair. They do not feed there, nor have their eggs or caterpillars been found in the fur. The caterpillars may live a normal life on plants where the eggs were laid by the adults on forays from their host.

class	**Mammalia**
order	**Edentata**
family	**Bradypodidae**
genus & species	***Choloepus didactylus*** two-toed sloth ***Bradypus tridactylus*** three-toed sloth, others

▽ *Look, no hands: a young two-toed sloth* **Choloepus hoffmanni** *giving a clear illustration of the 'backward' growth of hair, necessary for adequate insulation and waterproofing of the animal.*

Robert C Hermes

▽ *Individual sloth hair showing the one-celled algae, which make sloths look green.*

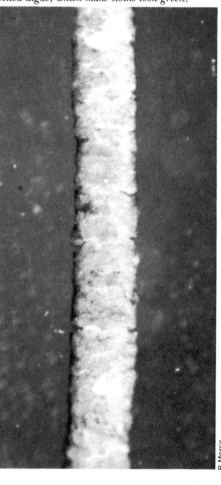

P Morris

Sloth

▮ 2-toed
(Choloepus didactylus)

▨ 3-toed
(Bradypus tridactylus)

Sloth bear

Sloth bear meditation in Kaziranga Park, India

Sloth bear

The sloth bear or Indian bear does not look like a typical bear because of its long, shaggy hair and thick, loose lips. The feet have blunt, curved claws up to 3 in. long. The hair is particularly long on the back of the neck and between the shoulders. The coat is predominantly black or blackish-brown, occasionally reddish. The long muzzle is dirty white or grey and there is a characteristic white, sometimes brown U- or V-shaped mark on the chest. Sloth bears grow up to 6 ft long, of which 7—8 in. is tail, and they stand 3 ft at the shoulder. They can weigh up to 250 lb. Females are smaller than the males but have denser fur.

Sloth bears live in Ceylon and in India from the south to the Himalayan foothills.

Slow bears

In Ceylon sloth bears are found in low country of the dry zone and in India they live in lowland jungles; they are rarely found at any great altitude. They are active mainly at dusk and dawn and often at night. They keep well away from human settlement and sleep in the cover of low vegetation or among rocks. The usual gait is a slow, shambling walk but when necessary sloth bears can break into a gallop and move faster than a running man.

Vacuum-eaters

Sloth bears feed on a wide variety of food, including insects, particularly termites and their larvae, carrion, birds' eggs, fruit, flowers and roots. They climb well, scaling trees to rob the nests of bees and birds. To some extent their diet varies with the season. In the wet season when the ground is soft termite hills are easy to break open and there are plenty of small animals to be found under fallen logs or in leaf litter. When the ground is baked hard and small animals are hard to find, the sloth bears live more on fruit.

Several mammals have taken to feeding on ants and termites, including another carnivore, the aardwolf (p 4). The sloth bear catches termites in a very different way to that used by the other ant-eating mammals. Common features of these animals are a long snout, a long tongue and teeth that are either small or missing. When they have broken open a termite hill they literally wipe up the termites with their sticky tongues. The sloth bear works on a vacuum-cleaning rather than a mop principle and sucks up the termites. The muzzle is adapted for this purpose. The nostrils can be closed, the inner upper pair of incisors are missing and the loose lips can be formed into a tube. When a sloth bear has broken into a termite's nest it inserts its head and blows violently, driving away dust and debris, and then sucks up the termites and their grubs. The sucking and blowing can be heard up to 200 yd away.

Carried by mother

Mating of sloth bears takes place all the year round in Ceylon, but appears to be confined to June in India. Courtship is boisterous but after mating the male is driven away. Usually two cubs, sometimes one and rarely three, are born 7 months later in a den among boulders or in a cave. When 2—3 months old they leave the den and accompany their mother. They sometimes ride on her back clutching the long hair between her shoulders. One sloth bear was chased for 3 miles with cubs on her back. The cubs stay with their mother for 2—3 years.

Dangerous when scared

The sloth bear is one of the most dangerous animals in the jungles of India and Ceylon and Ceylonese villagers are said to fear it more than any animal except a rogue elephant. Yet attacks are due to the sloth bear being frightened by the sudden appearance of a man. Its vision and hearing are not very good, so if it is approached from downwind, the sloth bear may not notice a man's approach until man and beast almost trip over each other. Then, in a panic, the sloth bear charges, knocks the man flat and mauls him before rushing off.

The dangerous nature of the bear almost certainly explains how little was known about it, and this ignorance also explains why it is called sloth bear. Skins of this bear were sent to Europe by big-game hunters towards the end of the 18th century. The notes accompanying the skins spoke of an animal with a trunk-like snout that swung acrobatically through the branches in the jungles of India and Ceylon. It was also said to cry like a child. The first scientists to examine the skins were content to refer to them as 'the nameless animal'. Dr George Shaw of the British Museum influenced by the descriptions of the animal swinging through the trees, classified it among the sloths. The mystery was solved when in 1810 a live bear reached Paris and for the first time it was realised that this animal was truly a bear and a very active one indeed; but the name sloth bear given by Shaw persisted.

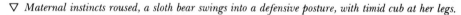

▽ *Maternal instincts roused, a sloth bear swings into a defensive posture, with timid cub at her legs.*

San Diego Zoo

class	**Mammalia**
order	**Carnivora**
family	**Ursidae**
genus & species	***Melursus ursinus***

Slow-worm

The snake-like slow-worm, alternatively known as the blind-worm or dead adder, is in fact a legless lizard. Internally there are vestigial shoulder- and hip-girdles, evidence that its ancestors once moved on four legs. A slow-worm has eyelids like other lizards, the two halves of its lower jaw are joined in front, another lizard characteristic and its tongue is notched, not forked like that of a snake. An average large slow-worm is about 1 ft long, the record is a 20.6in. female.

The head of a slow-worm is small and short, not so broad as the body immediately behind it and larger in the male than the female. Fully-grown males are more or less uniform in colour above and on the flanks. They may be light or dark brown, grey, chestnut, bronze or brick red and one variety is even copper-coloured. The belly usually has a dark mottling of blackish or dark grey. The female often has a thin dark line down the centre of the back and another on the upper part

underground ensures fairly constant temperature conditions.

The slow-worm is not inappropriately named. More often than not when we come upon it, it will lie motionless, making no attempt to escape. At most it may move away in a leisurely manner and generally its actions are slow and deliberate. Occasionally, however, by contrast, it will move with astonishing speed.

In October the slow-worm hibernates in an underground burrow, in a hollow beneath a large stone, or even beneath a pile of dead leaves. As many as 20 may be found in one hibernaculum, the largest being underneath, the smallest on top.

Slow-worms cast their skins or, more correctly, their cuticle, about four times a year. The frequency of sloughing depends upon whether or not it is a good slug year, the chief food of the slow-worm, the shedding being in response to the need for more space for the growing body. The skin is shed whole as in snakes. Although a slow-worm readily sheds its tail the new tail is shorter and never as perfect as the old one. There is usually a ragged end to the old part, the narrower new part appearing as if thrust inside the fringe of old scales.

moment of birth or shortly afterwards. Litters of 6–12, but as few as 4 or as many as 19 young have been recorded. They are born in late August or September, but if the weather is cold this may be delayed until October or later. The young are up to $3\frac{1}{2}$ in. long, silver or golden in colour with black underparts and a thin black line running down the middle of the back. Very active, they are able to fend for themselves from the moment of birth, catching insects, but showing a marked preference for any slugs small enough to eat.

Slow-worms have been known to live in captivity for up to 30 years or more, the record being held by one that lived in the Copenhagen Museum for 54 years.

Numerous enemies by man
Probably thousands of slow-worms are killed each year by man under the impression they are young adders. The slow-worm has many enemies, especially when young. Its main enemies are hedgehogs and adders. Frogs, toads, lizards and small snakes also eat it, as well as foxes, badgers and rats; and many birds, particularly birds-of-prey, and even the mistlethrush has been seen to take one.

▽ *Spritely youngsters: black-striped and golden or silver coloured, young slow-worms are able to fend for themselves from birth.*

SC Bisserot

of each flank, and her belly is usually black.

The slow-worm is found throughout Europe including the British Isles and eastwards into the Caucasus, Asia Minor and northern Persia. In Scandinavia and Finland it extends as far as latitude 65°N. It is also found in North Africa.

A variety of the slow-worm, known as the blue-spotted slow-worm, is widely distributed over Europe including the southern counties of England. The colour which may vary from a light blue to deep ultramarine may be present in spots or stripes, sometimes so closely set that the animal appears blue all over. All blue-spotted slow-worms are males.

Name not inappropriate
The slow-worm lives in open woodlands, commons and heathland. It is seldom seen during daylight apart from the spring and late summer or autumn. It spends the daytime under flat stones or logs or in burrows sometimes as deep as a foot below the surface, often lying in the earth completely buried except for its head. Life

The gardener's friend
The slow-worm eats spiders, small earthworms and tiny insects. There is a marked preference for the small white slug *Agriolimax agrestis* so often a pest on tender green vegetables. This is consumed in quantity, but where this slug is missing the slow-worm takes others. The prey is seized in the middle and chewed from end to end. The slow-worm also eats snails. The principal feeding time is soon after sunset, or after rain, when the slugs themselves come out to feed.

Ovoviviparous female
Mating is from late April to June, when there is a great deal of fighting between the males, each trying to seize the other by the head or neck. Once a hold has been obtained there is much writhing and rolling together. In mating the male seizes the female by the neck and twines his body around hers. The female is ovoviviparous, the eggs hatching within the body. On rare occasions the eggs are deposited before hatching. The young are enclosed within a membranous envelope which is punctured by a feebly developed egg-tooth, either at the

Deceptive appearance

Since the slow-worm's snake-like appearance can so easily deceive us, it is possible that other animals it is likely to encounter in the wild can make a similar mistake. Alfred Leutscher, writing in the *Illustrated London News* for June 3, 1950, tells the story of how he once placed a slow-worm in a vivarium containing three tame common frogs. They made repeated attempts to swallow the 'worm'. 'Suddenly these frogs began to behave as if frantic with fear, making every attempt to escape and dashing madly against the glass sides of their enclosure.' He came to the conclusion that the frogs had at first taken the slow-worm for a likely meal and had then mistaken it for a snake.

class	**Reptilia**
order	**Squamata**
suborder	**Sauria**
family	**Anguidae**
genus & species	*Anguis fragilis*

Slug

Broadly speaking a slug is a snail without a shell. This is, however, not strictly correct because it may have a vestigial shell, usually hidden within the body. Slugs belong to the Pulmonata, a large group of land and freshwater molluscs that breathe by means of a lung. There are three types: keelback slugs, roundback slugs and shelled slugs, forming the families Limacidae, Arionidae and Testacellidae respectively. The first are named for the ridge or keel on the upper surface of the body towards the hind end. Behind the head with its four tentacles the back is covered by a roughly elliptical mantle-shield perforated by the respiratory pore

▽ *Month-long incubation nearly over,* **Limax flavius** *eggs with embryos visible (approx ×5).*

and it can creep through much smaller holes than a snail. So slugs live in damp places and some species spend most of their lives underground. They are most active at night, or by day when it is wet, and some regularly return to the same 'home' after feeding. Though most feed near ground level, some are good climbers and regularly ascend trees to heights of 30 ft or more; the tree slug, *Lehmannia marginata*, formerly known as *Limax arboreum*, and field slug, *Agriolimax agrestis*, are two such climbers. The silver trails of slime running up and down some tree trunks attest to these activities, but the slug may take a more rapid route for the descent and lower itself many feet through the air on a string of slime. Such slugs spend the day in knotholes, coming down to the ground at dusk and climbing up again about dawn.

▷ *A roundback,* **Arion ater**. *Although called the large black slug, its colour is very variable.*

other and devouring each other's slime until they come to lie side by side. The great grey slug *Limax maximus*, up to 4 in. long, concludes this circling in a particularly spectacular manner. Climbing first up a tree or wall, the two slugs circle for a period of $\frac{1}{2}-2\frac{1}{2}$ hours, flapping their mantles and eating each other's slime. Then suddenly they wind spirally around each other before launching themselves heads downward into the air on a thick cord of slime perhaps 18 in. long. Now the penis of each is unrolled to a length of 2 in. and entwined with the other into a whorled knot. Sperm masses are exchanged after which the slugs either fall to the ground or re-ascend their life-line, eating it as they go. The eggs are laid soon afterwards in some damp recess such as under a stone or among roots. The soft amber eggs, about $\frac{1}{5}$ in. across, hatch in about a month.

Many enemies

Despite their unpleasant slime, slugs are eaten by a variety of predators, including frogs, toads, hedgehogs, ducks, blackbirds, thrushes and other birds. Ducks are especially good for controlling the numbers of slugs. Slow-worms and various insects also take their toll. Though sheep are not deliberate predators of slugs, they do eat them accidentally and in doing so may become infected with lungworm, a parasitic nematode, whose larvae have formed cysts in the foot of the slug.

Universal panacea

For many centuries slugs have been regarded in folk lore as a sovereign remedy for a variety of ailments, eaten alive or boiled in milk for the cure of tuberculosis, for example, or in the form of ashes to relieve such diverse ills as ulcers, dysentery or hydrocephalus. The internal shell, or the little chalky grains representing it, were often regarded as particularly efficacious and, as Pliny recorded, quick relief could be obtained if the granules were placed in a hollow tooth. Warts even now are the target of various odd forms of treatment and one in recent use, at least until the turn of the century, if not later, involved the use of slugs. The method was to rub the wart with the slug and then to impale the mollusc on a thorn. As it died and withered away, so did the wart. One may doubt the value of these old remedies, but there are many people today who seek 'solace in a slug'.

GS Giacomelli

on its right margin. In the keelback slugs this opening lies behind the middle of the mantle shield. In the roundback slugs the pore is farther forward. The tiny shell is a flattened oval, horny and with little lime in it, hidden under the mantle shield in the keelback slugs, but usually reduced to a number of separate chalky granules in the roundback slugs. An exception is seen in the North American roundback slug **Binneya** *in which there is an external spiral shell. The largest of these slugs may be 8 in. long, as in* **Agriolimax columbianus** *of North America.*

In the third group, the shelled slugs, there is a small shell visible on the surface towards the rear of the animal. A shelled slug may be anything up to 5 in. in length. Its mantle, heart and kidney lie under the shell towards the broad rear, instead of towards the front as in the other two families and a groove runs forward from the mantle on either side of the body, giving off branches to the back and flanks.

Tree climbers

Through having such a useless, almost non-existent shell a slug is more vulnerable to predators and, more important, perhaps, to drying up. However, the animal's load is lightened, its need for calcium is much less

Other food than seedlings

Although hated by the gardener slugs may be vastly more numerous in his garden than even he is aware and, taking them as a group, very little of their food consists of the plants he has cultivated, except where there are few alternatives. Some slugs feed almost entirely on fungi, eating little or no green food and then only when it is dying or rotting. Many slugs are omnivorous and are attracted by fungi, greenstuff, tubers, carrion, dung, kitchen refuse or the metaldehyde-baited bran put out to kill them. They are drawn to such foods over distances of several feet by the odour, a slug's organs of smell being in its tentacles. In confinement, slugs may turn upon each other, but the shelled slugs are particularly notable for their predacious habits. They are most common in well-manured gardens and live underground most of the time. They feed by night on earthworms and to a lesser extent on centipedes and other slugs, seizing them with their needle-like teeth and swallowing them whole.

Aerial courtship

Slugs are hermaphrodite and although self-fertilisation can occur a two-way exchange of sperm between mating pairs is usual. In the first stages of mating, roundback and keelback slugs typically trail around each other in a circle, constantly licking each

phylum	**Mollusca**
class	**Gastropoda**
subclass	**Pulmonata**
order	**Stylommatophora**
family	**Limacidae**
genera	*Limax, Agriolimax, Lehmannia, Milax*
family	**Arionidae**
genera	*Geomalacus, Arion*
family	**Testacellidae**
genus	*Testacella*

▽ *Flamboyant sexual display: after a $\frac{1}{2}$—$2\frac{1}{2}$-hour courtship of mantle-slapping display and slime-eating, a pair of slugs dangle on a cord of slime, their bodies constantly writhing at a pace that puts their usual slow movements to shame, both rotating back and forth in a semi-circle.*

▽ *They then extrude their sex organs by turning them inside out, as one turns out a glove finger. Slugs are hermaphrodites, so copulation is a sperm exchange. They can, however, fertilise themselves in adverse conditions. One organ is extended at right, the other shows between the slugs' heads.*

▽ *The fully extended sex organs assume an irregular shape and become pearly white with iridescent shades of pink, blue and green, then the slugs exchange sperm masses.*

▽ *The reproductive organs, now about 3 in. long, are still tightly intertwined. At this stage the slugs still twist and turn, as if engaged in a ritual dance.*

▽ *Mating complete, the happy couple re-ascend the rope of slime, eating it as they go. The eggs are laid soon afterwards, in a damp place, usually under a log or stone.*

Photos by Lynwood M Chace

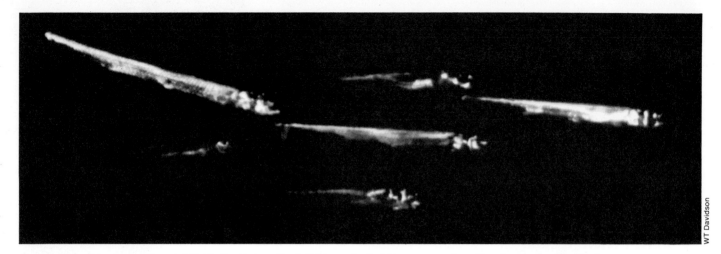

*△ Their light-dispersing equipment foiled by the photographer's lights, a school of **Osmerus mordax** shine clear in the Atlantic gloom.*

WT Davidson

Smelt

Smelts are small silvery fishes that seem to be able to live equally well in the sea and in estuaries. They are remarkable for their large numbers and many end up inside the gut of the larger fishes.

The European smelt is up to 8 in. long, and slim, with a pointed head and silvery body, olive-green on the back with a slight blue-green tinge on the fins. The jaws are large, the lower jaw jutting beyond the upper. There are fine teeth in the jaws, larger in the lower jaw than the upper, conical teeth on the roof of the mouth and several large fang-like teeth on the tongue. The dorsal fin is set far back and there is a small adipose fin just forward of the slightly forked tail fin.

The European smelt is found from the Seine to the Baltic. A similar species lives off the Atlantic coast of North America, from the Gulf of St Lawrence to Virginia. The candlefish, another species of smelt which grows to 12 in., lives on the Pacific coast from Alaska to Canada, and the surf smelt, from Alaska to California. One of the smallest is the 3in. Sacramento smelt of the San Francisco area. The remainder of the 13 species of smelt live in the North Pacific. There are no smelts in the southern hemisphere.

Fresh and salt water fishes
Smelts live in large shoals in coastal waters and in estuaries, and are rarely found far from the shore. In European waters some shoals spend their whole lives in the larger estuaries. Young smelts are often found in pools between tidemarks. The European smelt is said to be delicious to eat, despite its strong smell of cucumber which is especially pungent when its skin is damaged.

In parts of Europe, smelts have become landlocked permanently in fresh water. This has also occurred in North America. Moreover, the Atlantic smelt was introduced into parts of the Great Lakes and became numerous enough also to be fished commercially. In California there is a freshwater smelt that spends almost its whole life in the Sacramento River, yet the same species in Japan lives in the sea and only migrates into rivers to spawn.

Eggs with sticky flaps
The shoals of adult European smelts congregate around large estuaries in late winter to enter the rivers for spawning, which begins in March in the British Isles, later on parts of the Continent. The spawning runs are the time smelts are caught commercially. The males at such times develop small tubercles on their scales. After spawning they return to the sea but the young, hatching from the eggs, remain in the estuaries until the end of the summer. Development follows the normal pattern for this type of fish but the eggs are peculiar. They are pale yellow, $\frac{1}{20}$ in. diameter and they sink to the bottom. They are enclosed in a double membrane and as they sink the outer layer breaks away in part and the loose part becomes turned back. Its inner surface is sticky and adheres to stones and other hard objects, anchoring the eggs, which hatch 8–27 days later, depending on the water temperature. Each newly hatched larva is $\frac{1}{4}$ in. long but grows to nearly 3 in. by the end of the first year.

Predacious smelts
As we could expect from their batteries of teeth, smelts are predacious. The young smelts feed on tiny crustaceans, especially copepods, and on fish larvae. They also take small worms. They soon graduate to taking young herring and the young of other fishes, such as sprats, whiting and gobies, as well as a variety of crustaceans, from copepods to shrimps.

Caught in large numbers
Smelts everywhere are important in the food chains of larger fish-eating species. The numbers in which they are found has been well expressed by Earl S Herald. He quotes the case of the 3in. Sacramento smelt, of which 60 000 have been caught in Chinese shrimp nets in a 3-hour fishing period. In the Columbia River, farther north, tons of smelts are caught each year on their spawning runs. In North America also, in former times, the early Indians caught the candlefish in large numbers. This has a very oily flesh. The fish was dried and when tied to a stick could be lighted and used as a torch.

Disappearing trick with mirrors

There is a seeming contradiction in a fish being preyed upon by all and sundry yet continuing to exist in teeming numbers. Animals living in large herds on land, or birds flying in large flocks, can be shown to enjoy safety in numbers. A predator attacking them tends to be confused by their numbers, so they have to single out their victim and cut it off from the rest in order to make a kill. Those who have studied fishes, however, assure us that a solitary fish needs less efficient camouflage than fishes living in shoals because it presents so small a target compared with a shoal.

There are few silvery-sided land animals because as the sun moves across the sky the direction of the brightest light moves through many angles. An animal with silvery sides might be invisible while the sun is directly overhead but its flanks would stand out strongly at all other times of the day when light strikes from different angles.

A fish like the dace lives in clear water and its silvery sides reflect its surroundings like a mirror so that from any angle the fish looks like its background and is hard to see. Smelt live in the slightly dirty, or turbid, waters close inshore or in estuaries. They live in a world of scattered light. Under their scales are platelets of crystals and the angle these make with the surface ensure that a smelt swimming in the normal position can only be seen in silhouette by anything immediately underneath and looking up. From any other angle the light reaching the eye from the platelets has the same intensity as the light coming from behind the body. So the fish looks as if it is not there. This gives them something of the order of 99% protection.

class	Pisces
order	Salmoniformes
family	Osmeridae
genera & species	*Hypomesus olidus freshwater* *H. pretiosus surf* *Osmerus eperlanus European* *Thaleichthys pacificus candlefish* *Spirinchus thaleichthys Sacramento* others

Snakehead

Snakeheads are rather distinctive fresh-water fishes of Africa and southern Asia which are not very closely related to any other fish. Their nearest relatives are the perch-like fishes. They have long bodies, cylindrical in front, and almost circular in cross section but slightly compressed from side to side towards the hind end. They have large reptilean looking heads with a jutting lower jaw and a wide gape to the mouth which is armed with numerous teeth. There is the usual pair of double nostrils and in each pair the front nostril is tubular. The dorsal fin is soft-rayed and runs from just behind the head almost

are tiny pouches which are well supplied with a network of fine blood vessels that take up oxygen. Snakeheads can travel overland —by wriggling their bodies and by making rowing movements with their short, broad pectoral fins. When the ponds in which they live dry up, they bury themselves in the mud to a depth of 1—2 ft. It is then that local fishermen, armed with knives, slice out the mud to find them.

Snake throw to catch prey

When first hatched snakeheads feed on small plankton such as water fleas, rotifers and crustacean larvae. As they grow they take larger plankton including insect larvae and when about 2 in. long they begin to feed on small fishes, as well as insects and their larvae. When mature they feed almost

surface. In some species the males guard the eggs, and the larvae for a while, but they do not build a nest or show any other signs of parental care. Once the young fishes are able to swim on their own they hide among the water plants, a habit which then continues throughout their lifetime since snakeheads, like the pike, spend much of their time concealed among vegetation from which they emerge to seize their prey.

Baton charges

Snakeheads are important food fishes in southern Asia and have been introduced into parts of the United States where they are now flourishing. Because they are air breathers they can stay alive for days on end out of water and so remain fresh until

▽ *The Asiatic snakehead—slow-stalking, serpent-striking hunter of foul and stagnant waters which breathes air and can crawl overland.*

John Tashjian at Steinhart Aquarium

to the tail and there is a similarly long anal fin. The body is usually mottled with brown, sometimes with tinges of red. There are often distinctive grey, brown, and black markings along the body in the form of irregular bands or in the African species, V-shaped markings, or else there are large spots, sometimes in a row along each flank. This disruptive pattern makes the fishes blend with their background as they rest along the water plants. The smallest species is about 6 in. long, while others are up to 3 ft, and in the larger species there are exceptional individuals that grow to 5 ft long.

The Asiatic species range from Ceylon through India to southern China and southeast Asia and the Philippines.

Fishing with knives

Snakeheads live in foul and stagnant waters coming to the surface at intervals to gulp in air. Inside the gill chamber on each side

entirely on other fishes which they stalk stealthily, approaching them from the front. Then they bend themselves into an S-shape, and throw their heads forward with a sudden jerk to seize their prey. Adult snakeheads are voracious creatures; they eat frogs and even tackle water snakes.

Desultory parental care

They begin to breed when about a year old. A pair of snakeheads clear the waterplants over a small area. The females then shed their eggs into the water almost at random and the males do the same with their milt. The eggs are $\frac{1}{16}$ in. diameter and contain oil droplets so they rise to the surface and float. They hatch in 2—3 days, the larvae continuing to feed on the yolk sac for another 6—8 days, during which time they float belly-up on the surface. After this they are able to swim normally and they grow fairly rapidly, but they make frequent visits to the surface to gulp air and where they are numerous the water appears coloured as a constant procession of larvae rise to the

they are sold or needed for cooking. This is important in areas where few families have a refrigerator. Snakeheads are said to be able to live for months out of water, breathing air and deriving nourishment from the fat stored in their bodies. In the fish markets they are put out for sale on woven trays, and Earl S Herald has described how in the Philippines the women selling the fish have to periodically belabour them with a club to keep them from squirming off their trays. She calls attention to her wares in a singing monotone, beating time at intervals by landing blows of her club on the fish.

class	**Pisces**
order	**Channiformes**
family	**Ophicephalidae**
genera & species	*Channa asiatica* *Ophicephalus africanus* *O. punctatus, others*

2125

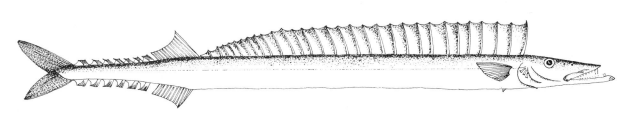

Wandering hunter: snake mackerel **Gempylus**.

Snake mackerel

Had a snake mackerel not jumped onto the Kon-tiki raft few people outside scientific circles would ever have heard of these fishes. They are oceanic fishes living in moderately deep waters, and are related to the true mackerels. They have long, fairly slender bodies, and a long snout with a prominent lower jaw which ends in a pointed fleshy tip. The mouth is armed with fanglike teeth. The eyes are large. The body is covered with small smooth scales and small forked spines. The first dorsal fin, which begins just behind the head, is long and becomes gradually lower towards its hind end. It consists of spines joined together by membranes and just behind it is a second dorsal spine followed by a few finlets which each consists of an isolated spine with a membrane. The anal fin is also followed by a few finlets. The pectoral fins are small, the pelvics very tiny. The back is dark brown to black and there are violet tints on the flanks and belly. There are two lateral lines, one just below the dorsal fin, the other along the midline of the flank. Both are whitish in contrast to the fins and inside of the mouth, which are black.

One species **Nesiarchus nasutus,** *4 ft long, is found in the North Atlantic from near the surface to 3 600 ft.* **Gempylus serpens,** *which grows to 5 ft, is found in all tropical seas from the surface to a similar depth of 3 600 ft.*

Vertical and horizontal journeys

Like so many deepsea fishes the snake mackerels make daily vertical migrations appearing near the surface at night. The fact that the same species is found in Atlantic, Indian and Pacific oceans suggests that snake mackerels are great travellers. Little more is known of their way of life, especially in the deep waters. They are sometimes brought up on long lines and from examination of the stomach contents it is known that *Nesiarchus nasutus* feeds on the viperfish *Chauliodus*, snipe-eels and squid. Usually it is the younger individuals of this species that are found at the surface. *G. serpens* seem to feed on flying fishes. Several of those caught in the tropical Indian Ocean have had the remains of flying fishes in their stomachs and one was seen to catch a flying fish.

Another reason why it is suspected that snake mackerels are great travellers is that although they are typically fish of tropical seas, they often wander into temperate latitudes. *Nesiarchus nasutus,* for example, is sometimes taken in the Bay of Biscay and off the edge of the continental shelf to the west of the British Isles. It has several times been captured as far north as Iceland.

Year-round spawning

Gempylus serpens is believed to spawn throughout the year and two spawning areas have so far been located, one in the Caribbean and one off Florida. The young fish when $\frac{1}{3}$ in. long has a deep body of which about $\frac{2}{5}$ is taken up by the head which has very large eyes. The dorsal fin is higher in front than in the adult but otherwise the fins are much the same as when the fish is fully grown.

Lure of the lights

Although public attention was focused on the two snake mackerels that jumped aboard the *Kon-Tiki*, this was not a unique event. It suggests, among other things, that the habit of jumping from the water after flying fishes must be a normal habit. The second of the snake mackerels seized the white rope Thor Heyerdhal had tied around his waist, which may have flashed in the light of the lantern, giving the appearance of an air-borne flying fish, or the lantern alone may have attracted the fish as snake mackerels are sometimes attracted to ships' lights.

Medicine fish

Another member of the same family *Ruvettus pretiosus* is the *escolar,* also known as the oilfish, scourfish, or castor-oil fish. It is deeper bodied than the others and has a more normal mouth although it is still a large one. It also is found in all tropical oceans and also in the Mediterranean, at depths of 600 – 2 400 ft. The fishermen of Madeira and the Canaries that use long-line fishing commonly catch it. Its flesh is very oily. It is called castor oil fish because its flesh acts as a purgative.

It used to be said that the name *escolar* meant scholar but a later suggestion is that it is from the Spanish word meaning to scour or burnish. This may refer to the roughness of the skin due to the prickles, or it may be just coincidence that another name for this fish is scourfish.

class	**Pisces**
order	**Perciformes**
family	**Gempylidae**

▽ *Raaby, of the* **Kon-Tiki,** *holds the most publicized snake mackerel.*

▽ **Kon-Tiki** *under sail. The snake mackerel was attracted to her lights.*

Snake-necked turtle

The 30 species of snake-necked turtles are found in South America, Australia and New Guinea. Together with the side-necked turtles of South America, Africa and Madagascar, they make up the sub-class Pleurodira. They differ from the other turtles, subclass Cryptodira, in withdrawing the head and neck sideways into the shell instead of vertically. They bend the neck sideways and tuck the snout under loose skin on the shoulder. A pleurodire turtle cannot withdraw its head completely into its shell, unlike the cryptodires which can withdraw their heads out of sight.

The common feature of the snake-necked turtles, is their long necks. The neck is longest in an Australian snake-necked turtle, or tortoise, in which an individual with a 15in. shell may have an 11in. neck. A close relative of snake-necked turtles is called the 'stinker' because when alarmed it gives off a pungent odour from a gland at the base of each leg. The carapace of this turtle is dark brown above, dark yellow below. The neck is covered with warts and the eyes are yellow. The average length of the shell is 6 in. Another very long-necked turtle is the otter turtle or Cope's terrapin of Argentina, Brazil and Paraguay. It is generally blackish with a 7—8in. shell. The matamata of Brazil and the Guianas,

▽ *Full stretch: Australian snake-necked turtle* **Chelodina longicollis**, *its extended neck taking up nearly half of its total length of 10 in.*

Fully extended (above) a snake-necked turtle's neck is vulnerable. Retracted (below) it shows the unorthodox withdrawal which gave rise to the name.

is the strangest-looking turtle. Its shell, which may grow to 18 in. long, has three ridges, covered with small knobs. The neck is covered with folds of skin and the head is flattened with a very large mouth and a stalk-like proboscis.

Built-in schnorkels

Snake-necked turtles live in fresh water. The long, pointed snout allows several of the snake-necked turtles to breathe without showing their heads, and the long necks enable them to breathe in shallow water while resting on the bottom. The matamata lives in stagnant pools and the rare western swamp tortoise of Australia lives in flooded pot-holes near Perth. Other snake-necked turtles live in permanent, fresher water. Most snake-necked turtles spend the greater part of their time in the water. *Mesoclemmys gibba* of Trinidad, the Guianas and Brazil rarely leaves the water but the *carranchina* of Colombia can run quite quickly on land.

Aquatic vacuum cleaner

Snake-necked turtles eat small animals, carrion, and some plant food. The snapping turtle of northern Australian rivers feeds on fruit and berries that fall into the water from overhanging trees, as well as other plants and animals such as crayfish and frogs. Whereas most snake-necked turtles catch their prey by suddenly throwing

out their long necks, the matamata sucks in passing animals. It lies in wait almost invisible with algae obscuring the already broken outline of the body and opens its mouth wide so that small animals are engulfed as water rushes in. Unlike other turtles, the matamata has very weak jaws, but the mouth is very large and can be opened suddenly, while the neck is expanded to increase its volume.

Pile-driver female

The life history of the snake-necked turtles is not at all well known, especially of those that live in South America and New Guinea. Breeding habits have been observed among some of the Australian species. The best known is the Murray River turtle of south and west Australia. Egg-laying is carried out in much the same way as in the marine turtles. The female crawls anything up to 200 yd from the water's edge and digs a conical hole about 8 in. deep with her hind-feet. As each egg is laid a hindleg is inserted into the hole to arrange the egg on the growing pile. She lays between 10 and 20 eggs and when the clutch is complete the hind-legs are used to scrape soil into the hole. The soil is tamped down by the body of the turtle which is raised and dropped like a pile driver. When the turtle has finished the nest is almost impossible to find and in 3 months the young hatch and push their way to the surface.

Strange rare turtle

The western swamp turtle of Western Australia is very likely the rarest turtle. It is also one of the most interesting as it appears to be closely related to ancestral turtles. Unlike other snake-necked turtles, the swamp turtle has a short neck.

The first specimen of the swamp turtle was found in 1839 but the next did not come to light until 1907. Then a third appeared in 1953 in an area of clay swamps, called 'crabhole country' near Perth. The swamps dry out in summer and the turtles burrow into the clay to aestivate until the rains. After the discovery of the 1953 specimen a detailed search was made for this rare turtle. Some were found in neighbouring swamps and the land was made into a nature reserve. Since then a few more swamps have been found to harbour swamp turtles.

class	**Reptilia**
order	**Chelonia**
family	**Chelidae**
genera & species	**Chelys fimbriata** *matamata* **Emydura macquarriae** *Murray River turtle* **Hydromedusa tectifera** *otter turtle* **Pseudemydura umbrina** *swamp turtle, others*

Snapper

Some snappers are important food fishes and are often considered as game fishes as they are a tussle for the sea-angler to land. There are over 250 species. They are deep bodied fishes with a large head, somewhat flattened on top as it slopes up to meet the front of the dorsal fin. The mouth is large and the jaws, with their sharp teeth, slope down to the corners giving the fish a disgruntled look.

The name is derived from the way the landed fish suddenly and very forcibly opens and shuts its jaws as it is dying, which sometimes causes bad wounds to the hands of an unwary fisherman sorting his catch. They are up to 2 ft or more long and have squarish tails. The dorsal fin is spiny in front, soft-rayed in the rear portion. The anal fin has several spines in front of its leading edge, and the pelvic fins are well forward, under the pectorals. Some species are grey to greyish green but many are beautifully coloured red or rose or, like the emperor snapper, whitish with reddish-brown bands. Yellow is another predominant colour. The yellowtail snapper has a yellow tail and a yellow line along the flank; its back is blue with yellow spots. The lane snapper of Florida to Brazil is striped red and yellow and the mutton snapper of the West Indies is banded yellow and green. Snappers are found in all warm seas. The greatest number of species are found throughout the Indo-Australian area although many are also found in the tropical waters of the coast of Atlantic America.

▽ *Prowling through the coral on an ever-hungry quest for anything, animal or vegetable, that moves, a shoal of Indian Ocean snappers* **Lutjanus kasmira** *decorates the Assumption Island reef.*

L. Sillner

Small shoals

Most snappers move about in groups of less than a dozen. They live mostly in coastal waters, especially around coral reefs, at depths of 24–90 ft, sometimes as deep as 400 ft. They are also seen near mangrove swamps and docks, always ready to investigate a possible source of food. Snappers feed mainly at night. Their hunting method is to stalk living prey until a few feet from it, then to make a sudden dash, seize the prey and swim leisurely back to the starting point.

Snapping up trifles

Snappers are euryphagous, which merely means they refuse nothing edible. They feed mainly on fish, but they will take crabs, lobsters and prawns, barnacles, octopus and squid, brittlestars, sea squirts, pyrosoma, salps, sea butterflies, worms and molluscs. They also take a small amount of plant

Research into breeding seasons

In spite of the abundance of snappers little is known of their breeding habits. In tropical waters the temperature varies very little throughout the year. Off East Africa, for example, temperatures vary from 24–29°C, and snappers spawn throughout the year. In Indian waters breeding seems to coincide with the cold season following the onset of the northeast monsoon in September and October. Off tropical America there seem to be two breeding seasons for snappers.

It may seem contradictory to say little is known about the breeding habits and then to specify the breeding seasons. It is relatively easy to note when fish taken in nets are ripe. The males, even without gutting, can be tested for ripeness by gently pressing the flanks to see if milt flows out. To find out where spawning takes place, to net the eggs

Unpredictable poisoning

There is a kind of fish poisoning called *ciguatera*. Some of the symptoms are muscular pains, cramp, nausea, diarrhoea, and even paralysis. Early symptoms are a tingling of the lips and throat and a sensation reversal in which hot things in the mouth feel cold and cold things feel hot. Snappers are among the 300 or more species of food fishes that can cause *ciguatera*, yet snappers are generally good food fishes. *Ciguatera* is, in fact, sporadic and unpredictable and is probably caused by a fish eating a particular kind of blue-green alga, perhaps at a certain time of year or in a particular stage of the alga's growth. It can also be caused by carnivorous fishes eating herbivorous fishes that have eaten the alga, as the poison is cumulative in the fish's body. It is also persistent, for in experiments to

A solitary Red Sea snapper **L. mussellii** *with its flattened snout and large, downward-sloping jaws shut tight, swims below an overhanging coral.*

L Sillner

food including algae and leaves, the last of these being eaten probably for no better reason than that they were moving through the water. Snappers will also take scraps thrown overboard from ships including vegetable waste.

The kind of food taken depends very much on which prey animal happens to be plentiful. There is also a change of diet with age, the young snappers feeding mainly on small fishes. A study of the food of one species over a period showed that of the total food taken 62% was fish and 25% crustaceans. In another it was 49% fish, 12% crustaceans and a little more than 12% for squid and for plankton.

and larvae and to follow the life history of the fish is far more difficult.

Mature fish are not always in breeding condition. After spawning their reproductive organs are spent and the fish are in what is called a resting condition. After this the organs begin to increase in size again and the germ cells become active. A male fish not yet ripe may give out sperm, but when fully ripe—ripe running, as it is called—it gives out milt when even a slight pressure is applied to the flanks. A ripe running female gives out eggs when her flanks are squeezed but before that, when gutted, the size of the eggs shows whether she is ripe, nearly ripe or ripening.

test this poisoning snappers kept in aquaria for over a year still caused *ciguatera* when they were fed to animals.

class	**Pisces**
order	**Perciformes**
family	**Lutjanidae**
genera & species	**Lutjanus analis** *mutton snapper*
	L. aya *red snapper*
	L. sebae *emperor snapper*
	L. synagris *lane snapper*
	Ocyurus chrysurus *yellowtail snapper, others*

Snapping turtle

The snapping turtles of America are well named and they need to be handled with caution. A full-grown snapping turtle can easily break a pencil in two or severely maul one's hand. Snapping turtles are heavily built with large heads and limbs which cannot be retracted into the shell. The common snapping turtle, usually known as 'the' snapping turtle, has a shell length of up to 15 in. but it is proportionately very heavy and can weigh up to 50 lb. The tail is half the length of the shell and bears a row of scales like a crest on the upper surface. The feet are partly webbed and bear strong claws. The skin is greenish and the shell is often covered with green algae. The plastron, the underside of the shell, is reduced in size and forms a cross with the turtle's limbs fitting between the arms of the cross.

The common snapping turtle is found in the eastern half of the United States. The other snapping turtle, the alligator turtle, is restricted to the United States, from Illinois to Texas and east to Florida. The alligator turtle is one of the largest freshwater turtles and can grow up to 200 lb, larger weights of up to 400 lb being unconfirmed. The shells of the alligator turtles grow up to nearly 3 ft long and bear three ridged keels. Unlike the common snapping turtle the eyes are set on the side of the head and cannot be seen from above.

Belligerent and other turtles

Snapping turtles are more aquatic than most freshwater turtles and spend most of their lives in muddy ponds, lakes and rivers. Alligator turtles in particular are very lethargic, walking on the bottom rather than swimming and, when disturbed in the water, their one idea is to escape. It is only when snapping turtles are found on land that they are aggressive and common snapping turtles are quite likely to advance on their foes. Snapping turtles hibernate, but can sometimes be seen swimming in lakes under ice during the winter months.

Contrasts in turtles

The common snapping turtle actively hunts for its food, which consists of plants, carrion, insects, fish, frogs, ducklings and young muskrats. Live prey is caught with a quick thrust of the head and snap of the jaws and

Cold-blooded murder: not fast enough to evade a speedy head thrust, a water snake writhes its last in the gin-trap jaws of a snapping turtle.

Photo Library Inc

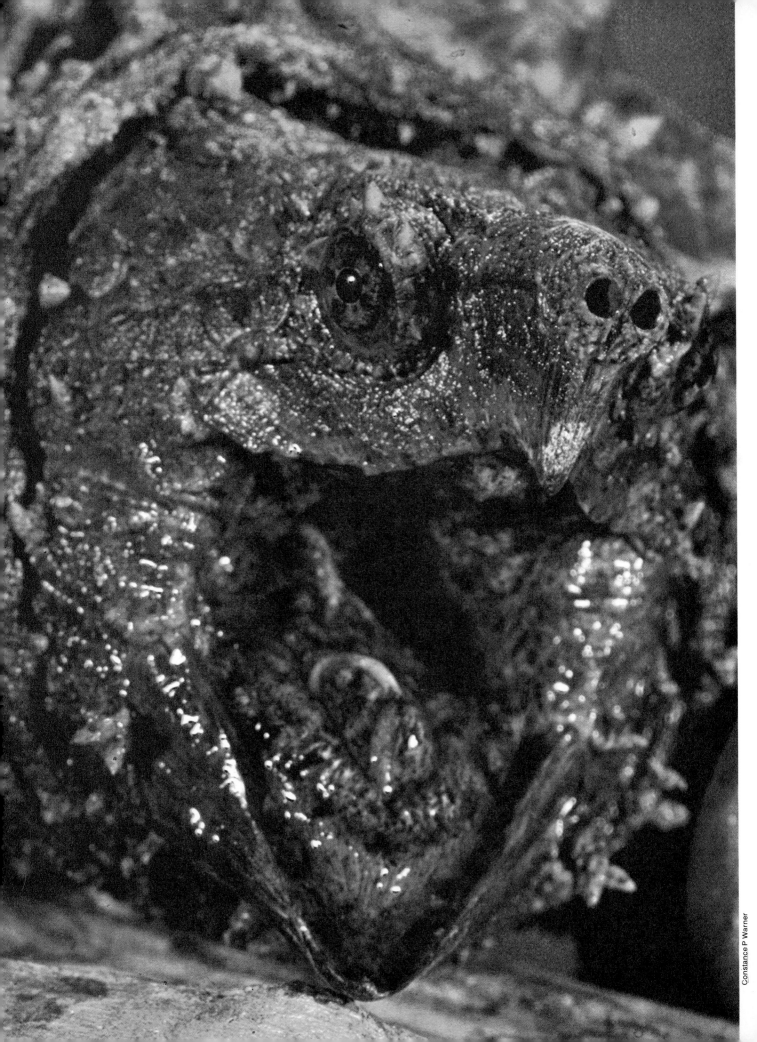

◁ *Open deceit. An alligator turtle opens its mouth to display its wriggling, worm-like tongue, which acts as a successful lure for many small fishes. The turtle's tongue is forked into two fat, pink branches which stand out against the dark background of the inside of the mouth. The turtle lies half buried in the mud, well camouflaged by its dull brown colour and rough, often algae-covered, shell. There it lies in wait for small fishes, opening its mouth as they pass, and luring them in. Only small prey is caught in this way; larger prey is hunted actively in the same way as the common snapping turtle.*

▽ *An alligator snapping turtle, showing its rough, three-keeled, mud-coloured shell which protects it and camouflages it as it lies in the mud. The eyes of this turtle, which is one of the largest freshwater turtles in the world, are on the side of its head, unlike those of the common snapping turtle.*

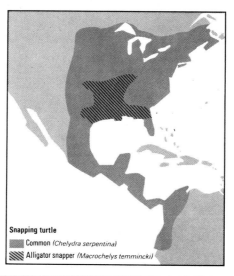

Snapping turtle

▨ Common *(Chelydra serpentina)*

▧ Alligator snapper *(Macrochelys temmincki)*

is then pulled apart by the mouth and claws. The fish-eating habits of snapping turtles often bring them into conflict with anglers or the owners of fish farms. Too many snapping turtles in a fish pond can lead to too few fish but some studies have shown that the harmful effect of snapping turtles on fish populations is often over-exaggerated. In many places, however, snapping turtles are trapped either because of their supposed depredations or to be turned into 'snapper soup'.

Unlike the common snapping turtle, the alligator turtle lies in wait for its prey, half buried in the mud and camouflaged by the algae growing on its shell. From this concealed position the alligator turtle lures small fishes into its mouth by a most remarkable piece of deception. The tongue is forked and the two branches are fat and wormlike. The turtle moves its tongue, making the wormlike tips wriggle and this attracts small fishes which are then promptly snapped up. Larger prey, including duck-lings, are also caught, but by more active hunting, not by means of the lure.

Over-wintering eggs

The common snapping turtle may crawl some distance from water to find a suitable place to make a nest. They seem to prefer open areas, and even cultivated land. The nest is dug with the hind feet and about 20 eggs are laid in each clutch. Hatching takes place in late summer, and eggs that are laid late may not hatch until the following spring. Breeding habits of the alligator snapper are similar but it lays its eggs, which may number from 17 to 44, near the water.

'Bloodhound' turtle

The carrion-eating habits of snapping turtles once led one of them to be used as an efficient, but gruesome, bloodhound. There was an occasion in the 1920's when a murderer hid the bodies of his victims by sinking them in the muddy waters of a lake. Although the police had a very good idea which lake had been used, they were hard put to find the bodies until an elderly Indian offered his services. It only took him a few hours to find each corpse yet his method was very simple. He released a large snapping turtle with a long line attached to its shell. When the line stopped playing out the Indian followed and, if he was in luck, the turtle would be found feeding on one of the murdered bodies.

class	**Reptilia**
order	**Chelonia**
family	**Chelydridae**
genera & species	***Chelydra serpentina*** *common snapping turtle* ***Macrochelys temmincki*** *alligator snapper*

◁ *Turtles in suspension. Common snapping turtles are poor swimmers and usually prefer to walk over the bottom. Although aggressive on land, they are quite the opposite in water, and often lie in wait for their prey.*

2133

Snipe

The snipe and their close relative the woodcock, belong to the family of wading birds, the Scolopacidae. Their general form is like that of other waders but their legs are not very long and the neck is fairly short. The bill is long and straight and the eyes are set well back on the head, giving snipe a characteristic appearance. The plumage is dark brown, mottled and barred.

The common snipe, 10½ in. long with a bill of 2½ in., is cosmopolitan, breeding in most of North America, Europe and Asia and in many parts of South America and Africa. The brown plumage is barred with black to give an effect of horizontal stripes, the crown is black and there are black stripes through the eyes. The underparts are whitish. The other snipes differ little in plumage. The great snipe is ½ in. longer than the common snipe and is very difficult to distinguish from it. It breeds in

Scandinavia, eastern Europe and western Asia. In eastern Siberia it is replaced by Swinhoe's snipe. The smallest snipe is the jack snipe, only 7½ in. long with a 1½ in. bill. Its bill is relatively shorter than that of the common snipe and its plumage is mottled rather than barred and has a metallic green and purple gloss. The jack snipe breeds in northeast Europe and northern Asia. The New Zealand snipe is unusual, nesting in the deserted burrows of other birds.

HM Barnfather

Undercover bird

Snipe live in open country, usually in wet places such as marshes, damp meadows and moors or in the swampy Arctic tundra. Their mottled plumage makes them very difficult to find among the low vegetation unless they are flushed, when they fly up on rapidly whirring wings and zig-zag before shooting away. The alarm call given as they flee is a harsh grating or a rapid squeaking 'ship-per, chip-per'. Snipe keep to the cover of vegetation, and are most active in the evening or early morning, as

Flexible bills

Snipe feed in the mud bordering lakes, rivers and marshes or in the damp ground of swamps where they probe for small animals. Their food is mainly worms but they also eat many kinds of insects, snails and woodlice. Like the woodcock, they can easily open their bills underground because the tips of the mandible are very flexible and can be forced apart even when the bill is buried to its base in the soil. Smaller animals can be eaten in this way without the bill being withdrawn.

head and bill and the white spot of the egg tooth. The chicks are fed by both parents and fly when 2 weeks old.

Drumming of snipe

The courtship display of snipe is called the drumming or beating flight, in which the snipe flies to a considerable height then dives rapidly with tail spread and the wings half-closed and beating slowly. This is accompanied by a soft, resonant drumming, which is repeated as the snipe

Eric Hosking

△ *A secretive bird caught dabbling unawares. Rarely seen unless flushed the common snipe, perfectly reflected in the water, gets ready to probe the mud for worms. It is a small wader and so is only able to feed along the water's edge. Its long straight bill is well adapted to its mode of feeding, the tip being flexible and able to be forced open even when buried deep into the mud.*

◁ *Well hidden among the foliage a common snipe sits on its nest, its beautifully mottled plumage helping to conceal it. All snipe except the New Zealand species nest on the ground in a hollow lined with grasses or in a tussock of rushes usually near water.*

is suggested by their large eyes.

The snipe of the northern hemisphere are migratory. The common snipe of North America, known as Wilson's snipe, flies down to Central America. The European common snipe migrates to Britain and southwest Europe. The pintailed snipe breeds in Siberia and migrates to India and southeast Asia. The great snipe migrates mainly to East Africa, south of the Sahara.

Hidden chicks

With the exception already mentioned of the New Zealand snipe that nests in the burrows of other birds, the snipe nest on the ground in a grass-lined hollow in a tussock or clump of vegetation. The great snipe differs from the others in having a communal display very much like the leks of the ruff (p 1996). Large numbers of males gather at a particular spot in the evening and display through the night, twittering in chorus, snapping their bills, or slowly flapping their wings.

The clutch consists of 4, sometimes 3, eggs usually olive brown with dark blotches. The female incubates the eggs for 19–20 days and the chicks leave the nest shortly after their down has dried. After the eggs have hatched, if disturbed, the adults run conspicuously to and fro or perform distraction displays. The chicks are, however, very inconspicuous, their down being brown and black, rather like a tortoiseshell cat. When disturbed they burrow headfirst into the coarse grass, which effectively hides the outline of the

glides and soars. The drumming is produced by air hitting the very rigid outer tail feathers whose vanes are held tightly together by an unusually large number of hooklets. The feathers vibrate rapidly to produce a humming note and the tremulous effect is added by the slipstream of air being 'pulsed' by the slowly beating wings. The pintailed snipe has 26 tail feathers, 12 more than the common snipe, the 8 outer pairs are stiffened for drumming.

class	**Aves**
order	**Charadriiformes**
family	**Scolopacidae**
genera & species	***Coehorypha aucklandica*** *New Zealand snipe* ***Gallinago gallinago*** *common snipe* ***G. media*** *great snipe* ***G. megala*** *Swinhoe's snipe* ***G. stenura*** *pintailed snipe* ***Lymnocryptes minumus*** *Jack snipe others*

2135

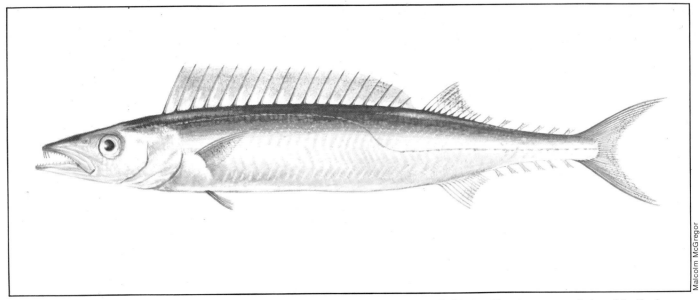

The vicious snoek is feared by many as it is able to inflict terrible wounds with the great fangs. The bite is said to prevent coagulation of the blood.

Malcolm McGregor

Snoek

The snoek is related to the castor oil fish and is an important food fish in the southern hemisphere. It is very like the snake mackerel in shape and its back is bluish-black, the rest of the body being silvery with faint dark bands across the flanks. The eye is golden. Snoek grow to 4 ft in length and weigh up to 20 lb.

'Snoek' is the Dutch word for a fresh-water pike and was used, for obvious reasons, by the early Dutch settlers in South Africa. In Australia and New Zealand it is known as barracouta, from its resemblance to the predatory barracuda. It is also sometimes called snook in Australia, sometimes pike or sea pike. There are other confusing uses of these names and in addition there is a snook **Centropomus parallelus** *in tropical American waters which belongs to a completely different family.*

The single species lives in waters of $10° - 20°C$, *from the surface to a depth of 240 ft. It ranges from the seas around South Africa to Tristan da Cunha, Argentina, Chile, New Zealand and Australia.*

Fish fanciers

Snoek swim in large shoals. They are active fishes which prey on other fishes. Off South Africa they feed especially on the sardine *Clupea sagax*, but any small fishes living near the surface are taken, including the young of their own species. They are also important predators of the South African pilchard *Sardinops ocellata* and the maas-banker *Trachurus trachurus*. Snoek are described as singling out individual fish then pursuing them for as much as half a minute, using their greater stamina to tire the smaller prey which can out-manoeuvre the snoek to escape. Sardines will often leap 2–3 ft out of the water when pursued by a snoek, which keeps up the chase when

both have fallen back into the water. Sometimes hundreds of sardines, each followed by a snoek, can be seen, all leaping out of the sea together. On occasions both prey and predator have leapt into a boat.

Blood transfusion for babies

Although voracious feeders which grow very fat during their feeding season, snoek, like so many other species, stop feeding as the breeding season approaches. The breeding season off South Africa is in the southern spring, but it varies slightly in other parts of the snoek's range. Some of the spawning grounds have been located, largely by examining the stomachs of predatory fishes containing snoek fry. A detailed study of the life history of the snoek has been made by BVD de Jager for the South African Division of Fisheries. Roes from the ripe snoek were taken and their contents, ova and sperm, were released into a sea water aquarium on board ship. The artificially fertilised eggs, $\frac{1}{25}$ in. diameter, floated at the surface because of the oil droplet in them. They hatched in 49 hours, and the newly hatched larvae, $\frac{1}{12}$ in. long, floated upside down at the surface, buoyed up by the oil droplet and the remains of the yolk sac. By the end of 9 days the larvae were $\frac{1}{6}$ in. long, after which time they died off. The difficulty was in finding food for them. They refused diatoms and brine shrimp larvae. Extract of beef liver, which was accepted by the larvae, fouled the water. The larvae were finally fed on drops of human blood (devoted scientists'!).

Huge catches

Snoek are caught by various forms of line fishing such as trolling and jigging. If there is a local abundance of prey fishes the snoek ignore the baits, but otherwise they will take any flesh from fish and squid to offal. The catches vary widely from year to year, for reasons not fully clear. There is a suspicion that there may be 7–9 year cycles of abundance and scarcity. On the other hand snoek are mainly fished from small vessels whose activities are very subject to the weather, so the cycles could be just due to

changes in the weather condition. So although it is an important food fish the total catches for South Africa have varied from 4 to 9 million lb per year. The returns for Australia are smaller, with an average catch of 4 million lb. The fish are eaten fresh, salted or smoked.

Tiger of the sea

During the Second World War when Britain was desperately short of food, quantities of snoek were sent from South Africa. One would have expected this to be greeted with gratitude but instead snoek became a comedians' joke and material for the cartoonist. One cartoon showed a housewife preparing to open a can of snoek while her husband stood by with an axe poised to deal with 'the tiger of the sea'. All this suggests the fish was not popular in Britain. This contrasts strangely with the account given in *Discovery* Report No 34. In November 1933, RRS *Discovery II* lay at anchor off Tristan da Cunha. Snoek were 'hovering' around the gangway lights at night so the scientists aboard started to fish for them and landed $\frac{3}{4}$ ton of them in 3 hours. 'The fish were placed in the ship's cold-store as soon as we finished cleaning them next morning, and provided at least one course per day for all who cared for them until we reached New Zealand some $2\frac{1}{2}$ months later.'

One of the basic problems in feeding hungry populations throughout the world is that people do not take readily to strange foods. The wartime jokes about snoek in Britain sprang almost solely from the fact that its people had not heard of snoek before, and one of the first things they did learn about it was it had fearsome teeth.

class	**Pisces**
order	**Perciformes**
family	**Gempylidae**
genus & species	***Thrysites atun***

Antarctic glider on outstretched wings: a pure white snow petrel flies over the pack ice searching the surface waters for fish and krill.

Snow petrel

The snow petrel, and its close relative the Antarctic petrel or Antarctic fulmar, nest farther south than any other birds. They have been found nesting in Antarctic mountain ranges many miles from open water. Only the great skua has been found farther south when one individual was seen flying around the South Pole.

As befits its home in the Antarctic, the snow petrel has a pure white plumage which is offset by its black eyes, bill and legs. It has even been said that the snow petrel is 'so white that it forms a contrast with the snow'. This may be an exaggeration but it does convey an idea of the whiteness of the snow petrel's plumage which makes it very difficult to see against the snow, as compared with a polar bear, for instance, which is more a dirty yellow.

Snow petrels are 16 in. long and are related to the fulmar of the North Atlantic, having the typical petrel bill with its tubular nostrils. They breed around the coast of the Antarctic continent and on the islands of the Scotia Arc as far north as South Georgia and Bouvetøya. The snow petrel is, therefore, very much an inhabitant of the pack-ice zone, yet its relative the Antarctic petrel, which has a similar distribution, has strangely, a brown-and-white-chequered plumage.

Birds of the pack ice

The life of the snow petrel is very closely linked with the drifting pack-ice of the Southern Ocean. As one sails southwards towards the Antarctic, snow petrels suddenly appear in large numbers as the ship approaches the pack-ice. They fly low over the waves in the same way as other petrels, while in the pack-ice itself they can be seen sitting in tight groups on floes, then all flying up together as if on a signal. The dependence on pack-ice explains their dis-tribution as the current from the Weddell Sea carries ice northwards around South Georgia and Bouvetoya. On the other hand snow petrels do not breed on Heard Island which is about the same latitude as South Georgia. The only snow petrel to have been seen on Heard Island arrived when the pack-ice came unusually close.

Although petrels are renowned for flying for exceptional lengths of time, they some-times land in the sea, bobbing up and down like corks. When there is a storm they prefer to ride it out on the wing, flying in the wave troughs for shelter.

Keen noses

Like other petrels, snow petrels feed on small animals living near the surface of the sea. Much of their feeding takes place at night and in the pack-ice they fish in the 'leads' and pools of open water between the floes. Most of the snow petrels' food is small crustaceans such as krill and amphi-pods but they also catch fish. It has been said that snow petrels eat more fish than most petrels and in one group of snow petrels that were examined 95% of the food they had caught was fish. While they are rearing their chicks they catch the immature stages of such fish as Antarctic cod (p 477), which live at the surface.

In general birds have a poorly developed sense of smell but that of the tube-nosed petrel is better developed than most, and the snow petrel also has larger olfactory organs than any other petrel that has been examined. This would suggest that the snow petrel finds its food by smell but it is difficult to see how the sense of smell can be of use in catching small animals by plunge-diving.

Snow butterflies

Snow petrels breed on sea cliffs or inland mountain faces, nesting on ledges or be-tween boulders. In the northern parts of their range, snow petrels can be seen flying around their nesting areas at any time of the year and even farther south snow petrels are to be seen when other petrels have dispersed out to sea for the winter. Throughout the time that the snow petrels are around the cliffs they can be heard calling, particularly at night. They have two calls, a raucous shrieking and a 'caw' repeated 4–5 times. There is also an aerial display called the 'butterfly flight' in which a snow petrel flies on rapidly beating, almost quivering wings. The butterfly flight is thought to have some significance in court-ship but as it is even performed by immature birds its function is obscure.

Just before the single white egg is laid the snow petrels disappear from the cliffs on a 'pre-egg laying exodus'. They go out to sea to feed and get enough food reserves for the female to form the egg and for the male to survive the first long spell of incu-bation. Incubation lasts 7 weeks and for a few days after the egg has hatched the fluffy chick is brooded. Then it is left alone except when the parents return at night to feed it. It flies at 6 weeks.

Nesting farthest south

For some years it has been known that snow petrels have nested in the Tottanfjella, a range of mountains 300 miles east of the Weddell Sea. This was the farthest south that any bird was known to nest, but more important than this, is the distance from open water. To get food for their chicks the snow petrels have to make a round trip of at least 600 miles, often against strong winds. In the southern summer of 1967/8 another colony of several hundred pairs of snow petrels and Antarctic petrels was found in the Theron Mountains, a range about the same distance from the sea as the Tottanfjella, but farther south, at latitude 79°. This is now the most southerly nesting place that is known.

class	**Aves**
order	**Procellariiformes**
family	**Procellariidae**
genus & species	***Pagodroma nivea***

A Thau: Bavaria

◁ *Feather-footed power: a female snowy owl.* △ *An incongruously idiotic stare. The large, nocturnal eyes are deceptive; snowy owls often hunt by day.*

Snowy owl

Although one of the most powerful owls, the snowy owl is not the largest. It is 20–24 in. long, considerably smaller than the eagle owl of Europe and Asia. In general appearance it is like a large barn owl but its plumage is whiter. Male snowy owls may be almost completely white or they may have some dark barring and spots. The females are larger than the males and their plumage is more extensively barred on the head, back, wings and underparts. Dark males may, however, be darker than light females. The feathers extend down the legs and they may even cover the claws. The bill also is almost obscured by feathers which, with the narrow, slit-like eyes, give the snowy owl a·stupid, self-satisfied, rather cat-like expression.

Snowy owls breed in the tundra of the Old and New Worlds. In America they range from the far north of Greenland to the southern shores of Hudson's Bay; in the Old World they breed in the north of Siberia, in northern Scandinavia, on the islands of Spitzbergen, Novaya Zemlya, Iceland and within recent years snowy owls have successfully colonised the Shetland Islands.

A new nesting ground

The home of the snowy owl is the barren, treeless wastes of the north, extending as far north as there is snowfree ground in summer. In the winter there is a general movement southwards. and this is quite spectacular in years when there is a shortage of food in the tundra. In these years they are found as far south as California, Bermuda, England and France, becoming spectacular additions to the local bird life.

In 1967 the snowy owl's breeding range took a well-publicised extension southwards when a nest was found on Fetlar, one of the Shetland Islands. For a few years prior to this snowy owls had often been seen on Fetlar and neighbouring islands, and had probably been induced to stay by the plentiful supply of rabbits and the similarity of the terrain to the Arctic tundra; the nesting area on Fetlar is rocky with low herbage. The pair continued to breed successfully in the following years. It is possible that snowy owls used to breed in the Shetland Islands as they were once common there before collecting took its toll, but there are no clear records of nesting.

Lemmings are main food

Snowy owls prey on a variety of small animals such as lemmings, mice, rabbits, and ground squirrels and on many birds, including oystercatchers, Arctic skuas, eider ducks, gulls and buntings, and occasionally they take insects, fish and carrion. The owls hunt from a perch on a rock or post, or quarter the ground on long glides with deep wingbeats, almost like a hawk. Birds are sometimes caught in the air.

In many parts of its range, the chief food of snowy owls is lemmings, although on Fetlar, for instance, it is rabbits. Lemming populations undergo vast cyclic changes about.every 4 years (p 1301) which has profound repercussions on their predators such as the snowy owl, the Arctic fox (p 80) and the pomarine skua (p 2159). As already mentioned, snowy owls migrate farther south in years of lemming scarcity, but in these years they may, like the skuas, completely fail to breed. On the other hand, when lemmings are abundant the owls may lay more eggs than usual.

Staggered hatching

Snowy owls make no nest but lay their eggs in a depression in the ground on a knoll or hillock that gives the sitting bird a good view of the surrounding country. Thus it is very difficult to approach a snowy owl's nest without disturbing the sitting bird. Even if it is possible to approach without being seen from the nest, the male will give the alarm from its look-out nearby. The alarm call is a harsh bark, repeated up to six times and if a human intruder approaches the nest the owls may dive at him or show a threat display in which the snowy owl lowers its body with feathers fluffed, wings spread and eyes glaring. Large birds such as ravens and greater black-backed gulls are chased away from the nesting area.

The number of eggs in a clutch is usually 5–8 but there may be as few as 3 or as many as 13, depending on the abundance of food. The female incubates the eggs for 32–34 days while the male stands guard and brings her food. Incubation starts as soon as the first egg is laid so the chicks hatch one after another and there may be a considerable difference in size between the oldest and youngest. The female feeds the chicks which beg for food by nibbling at her bill and feathers. As the chicks get older, the male also feeds them, instead of just handing the prey to the female, and the female goes hunting herself. The chicks leave the nest when nearly 3 weeks old and shelter under rocks until they can fly at about 7 weeks old. They stay together and continue to be fed by the parents for some time.

Snowy but camouflaged

Several animals, such as polar bears, snow petrels and Arctic foxes, which live in polar regions, have white fur or feathers, and this is related to the background against which they live. Snow petrels and polar bears are usually found amongst pack ice and Arctic foxes and snowshoe hares only have white fur during the winter. For the rest of the year, when the snow has gone, they have dark fur which also blends against the background. The white plumage of snowy owls seems completely wrong as they must be very conspicuous to their prey and they seem to contradict the usual rule of ground-nesting birds having good camouflage, until one realises that only the female sits on the nest. The female snowy owl is not such a brilliant white as the male and her barred plumage makes her inconspicuous against the lichens and grasses of the tundra.

Shetlands' snowy owls

◁ *A male snowy owl alights at its clifftop nest with a rabbit. The chicks show marked differences in sizes due to staggered hatching, a common condition in owls. Because of this the youngest and smallest chicks often fall victim to their elder brothers and sisters. The chicks leave the nest when nearly 3 weeks old.*

▷ *A snowy owl chick accepts a re-gurgitated pellet as food from its mother. Feeding the chicks on pellets is unusual and has only been noted before in barn owls. The pellet may be given as additional material, or it may be used as a substitute, to appease the chick when food is scarce.*

▽ *Three dozy snowy owls sit huddled together whilst a large chick threatens the youngest of the brood. The dark coloured chicks are well camouflaged against their surroundings. They usually remain perfectly still, and when grouped together like this, they look very like a pile of stones or a rock outcrop.*

Eric Hosking

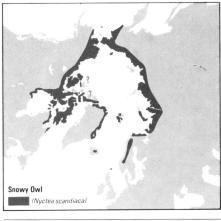

Snowy Owl
▮ *(Nyctea scandiaca)*

class	**Aves**
order	**Strigiformes**
family	**Strigidae**
genus & species	*Nyctea scandiaca*

R J Tulloch: Photo Res

Soft coral

Although soft corals are so frequently mentioned in books on marine biology, few authors agree on which of the many kinds of corals should be called soft corals. The following kinds have been variously included: the gorgonians or horny corals which include the sea fans, the alcyonarians and the antipatharians. These are all related to each other and also to reef corals. Most of them are not soft anyway, and the confusion is one that has been handed down from the days of the Greeks and Romans. Indeed, the only justification for treating soft corals under a separate heading is that the name appears so often in books on animals.

It was believed in Europe in those early days, and for many centuries after, that corals were soft while living in the sea but became hard when brought up into the air. There are no reef corals in the Mediterranean and the coral in question and the one to which the name was originally given was that now known as **Corallium**, the red or precious coral. This is one of the gorgonians. It forms red tree-like colonies with white polyps scattered over the surface and other, partly hidden polyps without tentacles between them. At the centre of the stem and branches is a hard calcareous core coloured red or pink, which is hidden within the fleshy part of the colony. The flesh is to some extent stiffened by red or pink spicules.

On p 621 **Corallium rubrum** was mentioned as a semi-precious coral related to dead man's fingers and was inadvertently included with it in the order Alcyonacea. Its correct place is in the order Gorgonacea, with the sea fans, which are also called soft corals by some people. When we speak of precious or semi-precious corals or of soft corals we cannot do so with any kind of precision. All three names are used differently by different people. Some of the precious or semi-precious corals belong to the Alcyonacea, some of them belong to the Gorgonacea. For the most part these are the same species that are referred to as soft corals, but again different authors use the term 'soft coral' to mean different things. Some even include sea pens among the soft corals. To avoid confusion therefore special attention will be given to one group only, the Gorgonacea, because the Alcyonacea, represented by dead man's fingers has already been dealt with, and so have the sea pens.

Flexible sea fans

The Gorgonacea live in all seas, from about lowtide mark to more than 12 000 ft but the vast majority are in waters of less than 3 000 ft depth, and especially where the sea bed is rocky. They are especially numerous in the warmer seas, and particularly so in the Malay Archipelago. They range

Ron Taylor

△ Underwater fauna with a yellow soft coral.   ▽ The red or precious coral **Corallium rubrum**.

G Mundey

△ *Soft coral with delicate polyps extended.*

▽ **Gorgonia:** *branched and brightly coloured.*

Ron Taylor

Ron Taylor

from small low colonies to immense branching colonies up to 6 ft high, the commonest colours being yellow, orange, red and purple. Where they live in shallow waters with a constant current the Gorgonacea tend to form fans at right angles to the current. In quiet waters, including deep waters, they are apt to branch freely in all directions, or else not to branch at all but form irregular masses. Their structure and way of life is similar to those of dead man's fingers, except that the red coral *Corallium rubrum* does not shed eggs into the water, as most of its relatives do. In May and June oval larvae squeeze their way out through the mouths of some of the polyps and swim away. Another species *C. nobile* is exceptional in being hermaphrodite.

All gorgonians, except for *Corallium,* have a horny core at the centre of the branches and stem. This is very flexible and is responsible for the tree-like skeletons of sea fans after their flesh has decomposed and fallen away. Such gorgonians fully justify the name of soft coral. Yet, as has already been indicated, it was the hard skeletons of the exception among gorgonians, the red coral *Corallium rubrum,* that originally determined that any corals should be called soft. It was also this red coral that figured prominently in the cultures of these early times.

Warding off the evil eye

There has been such a brisk and long-standing trade in red coral that it has become scarce in the Mediterranean. First it was used by the Gauls to decorate their helmets and weapons, the seas off the south of France being one of the chief places where it was fished. Others were off Corsica, Sardinia, Sicily and North Africa. A widespread trade in it sprang up about the beginning of the Christian era. In India especially it was esteemed for its sacred properties. The Romans used it medicinally. Branches of the coral were hung round children's necks to protect them from all dangers as well as to ward off illnesses.

How coral was born

These beliefs, which seem to us so futile, have their origin in Greek mythology. Medusa was a goddess whose singular quality was to turn to stone anyone who looked at her. Perseus finally cut off her head and cast it on the seashore. The water nymphs threw small bunches of seaweed at it for the fun of seeing them turn to stone. The seeds from these when returned to water gave rise to coral. According to Orpheus of Thrace, and Ovid, that is why coral 'even to this day turns into stone when it comes in contact with air, although it is soft so long as it is still submerged'. Minerva was so pleased with the exploit of her brother Perseus that she conferred on coral a number of virtues which guard people on journeys on sea or land, provide an antidote to poison and defeat spells.

phylum	**Coelenterata**
class	**Anthozoa**
order	**Gorgonacea**
genera	***Corallium, Eunicella, Gorgonia***

Soft-shelled turtle

The soft-shelled turtles are unlike other turtles because their shells are covered by a layer of leathery skin instead of horny plates. The shell is flat and almost circular, which gives some of them the alternative name of 'flapjack turtle'. The jaws are hidden under fleshy lips and the snout is drawn out into a tube-like proboscis. The fourth and fifth toes are elongated, clawless and are webbed to form paddles.

Soft-shelled turtles are found in many parts of Africa, Asia and America and fossils of one genus, **Trionyx**, have been found in many parts of Europe. Modern members of **Trionyx** are still spread over three continents. The spiny soft-shelled turtle is widespread in North America, from the St Lawrence to the Rocky Mountains. The front edge of its shell is lined with soft spiny tubercles. The upperside of the shell, which reaches 16 in. in length, is greyish-green with many small dark spots, often arranged in small circles. The Nile soft-shelled turtle ranges from

△ A retiring **Pelochelys bibroni**. Like other 'soft-shells', it has fleshy lips and an elongated snout.
▽ **Trionyx** paddling along with periscoped head. Apparently it can swim at 10 mph.

Palestine to the Congo and has a shell up to 2 ft long. Some of the African and Asian soft-shelled turtles have hinged flaps at each end of the plastron, the underside of the shell, which completely close up the shell when the head and limbs are withdrawn. The largest species is the long-headed soft-shelled turtle that ranges from North India to Malaya. Its shell reaches over 4 ft in length.

Supplementary breathing

Soft-shelled turtles usually live in fresh-water but the long-headed is apparently able to live on the shore. They are extremely active, perhaps as a result of their light-weight shells. They have been reported to swim at 10 mph and to be able to outrun a man on level ground. These turtles must be handled with care, as they can strike very rapidly, sometimes causing nasty wounds, but the long-headed soft-shell, which strikes like a snake, does no more than butt its adversary with its snout.

Although capable of bursts of great activity, soft-shelled turtles spend much of their time lying almost submerged in the muddy bottoms of lakes and rivers. They

Okapia

△ *A soft-shelled turtle breaks the surface as it stretches out its long neck to breathe in air through its long, tubular nostrils.* ▽ *Aquatic ugly: front view of a* **Trionyx.**

Klaus Paysan

△ *A turtle with a matching head and shell:* **Lissemys punctata.** ▽ *Its underside shows the plastron and the pair of strong, hinged flaps which close over the hind limbs when they are withdrawn.*

can stay underwater for long periods by stretching their long necks until the tube-like nostrils break the surface of the water, rather like a submarine's snorkel. They can also stay under by using a supplementary method of breathing: using both mouth and rectum as gills they extract oxygen from the water that is circulated through them.

Cutting or crushing

Like other freshwater turtles, such as the snapping turtles, the soft-shelled turtles live on a variety of food including plants, carrion and live animals. The main food of the spiny soft-shelled turtle is crayfish and aquatic insects and it is doubtful whether it ever harms angling interests as is sometimes asserted. The jaws of these turtles appear deceptively soft as they are hidden by fleshy lips. They are, in fact, very strong. In some species the jaws have a sharp cutting edge suitable for dealing with fish, while others have jaws with surfaces better suited for crushing the shells of molluscs.

Breeding mysteries

Very little is known about the breeding habits of soft-shelled turtles. Nesting takes place in spring or early summer in North America. The females leave the water to dig nests on land. These nests are similar to those of many other turtles: they are flask-shaped holes dug as far as the hind legs reach, which is up to 1 ft deep. Ten to twenty-five round white eggs are deposited in the nest and covered over. The length of the incubation period is not known, but some eggs do not hatch until the following spring.

Sacred turtles

Some of the soft-shelled turtles are greatly esteemed as food but others have been rigorously protected for religious reasons in Asia. For several centuries Mohammedans have kept a pond of *Trionyx gangeticus* at Orissa in India and there is a pond of *T. formosus* at Mandalay. A third collection of sacred turtles is held at Chittagong in East Pakistan. These are *T. nigricans* and are the only known examples of this species. These turtles are often very tame and will come to be fed by hand when called. In parts of Africa the Senegal soft-shelled turtle is kept for a more practical purpose. It is placed in wells to eat any refuse that falls in.

class	**Reptilia**
order	**Chelonia**
family	**Trionychidae**
genera & species	*Chitra indica* long-headed soft-shelled turtle *Cyclanorbis senegalensis* Senegal soft-shelled turtle *Pelochelys bibroni* Malayan soft-shelled mud turtle *Trionyx spinifera* spiny soft-shelled turtle others

Sole

The common sole is considered by some connoisseurs to have the best flavour of all fish but only after it has been dead 2—3 days (see plaice p 1786). Soles are tongue-shaped flatfishes in which the mouth is on the side of the head which projects forward of the mouth in a smoothly rounded curve. They lie on the left side. The dorsal fin starts on the front of the head and continues round the margin of the body to join the tail fin, the anal fin being nearly as long but starting behind the gill cover. Dorsal, tail and anal fins form a complete fringe. The underside of the head is covered with little white tags crowded together.

Most soles are up to 1 ft long but some are double this length. The usual colour of the upper surface is yellow, greyish-brown or dark brown with well-spaced darker spots or blotches or with dark bands. One of the more striking species is the naked sole of the American Atlantic coasts which has a zebra pattern, with close-set, reddish-brown crossbands.

They live mainly in shallow seas, on muddy or sandy bottoms, although a few species live in deep water, such as **Bathysolea profundicola** *which ranges from 900—3 800 ft. Most live in warm seas but some species, including the common sole of Europe, range into temperate seas as far north as the Faeroes. The hogchoker of America, 6 in. long with crossbands on the upper surface and spots below, lives in the sea from Carolina to Panama but sometimes enters fresh water.*

Patting the ground with its cheek

Soles lie on the bottom of the sea more or less buried in the sand during most of the day. They do this by strongly wriggling the body with an up and down undulatory movement, which digs a shallow trough and at the same time throws up sand that settles on the sole, partially hiding it. They normally become active at night, which is their main feeding time. Soles are also active by day when the skies are overcast or when the water becomes murky. Then they creep slowly along the bottom using the ends of the fin-rays with which their bodies are fringed. A sole searching for food raises its head slightly upwards and sideways, patting the sand from time to time with the underside of its head. Its eyes are small and, from the way the fish behaves, seem inefficient. A sole will stop and go back to examine any small object its undersurface has touched, feeling it with the lower surface of its head. The little white tags are sensitive, and are probably organs of touch, possibly also of taste, and the tubular nostril on the underside suggests that it may also use smell in searching for food. One nostril of the sand sole, for example, is surrounded by a rosette of swollen skin.

▷ *A common sole glides down to the sea bed.*

Noailles: Jacana

Digesting strings of beads

The sole feeds entirely on bottom-living animals and seems incapable of catching, or even of noticing anything swimming just off the bottom. Its upper jaw and teeth are feeble and most of its mouth is on the undersurface of the head. Small crustaceans, worms and molluscs make up the main part of its diet, and to these are added brittlestars and small bottom-living fishes such as sand eels and gobies. Prey is not seized by the mouth until the sole has been able to cover all or part of it with the front part of its head. Young soles feed on smaller crustaceans such as copepods and on fish larvae.

As long ago as 1740 a Mr Collinson was fascinated to find he had bought some soles, the bellies of which were 'hard and prominent, appearing to be filled with rows of some hard substance'. He opened them up and described what he found in the *Philosophical Transactions of the Royal Society, London*. The hard substance was 'found to be shell-fish. These, from the bulging of the shells and the intervening interstices, gave the intestines somewhat the appearance of strings of beads. On further examination some of them were found nearly dissolved, others partly so, but many of them whole'.

Flattened juveniles

The common sole and some other species move into deeper water for the winter but migrate back to shallow inshore waters in spring and early summer to spawn. The eggs, $\frac{1}{20}$ in. diameter, float well off the bottom. Each mature female lays about half a million eggs. The larvae are $\frac{1}{8}$ in. long when hatched and, as in other flatfishes, have a normal shape. As they grow they come to lie on the left side and the left eye migrates to the right side as in plaice. By the time they are $\frac{3}{4}$ in. long their bodies have become flattened and they have settled on the bottom.

What's in a name!

Relatives of the common sole are little fished: the solenette because it is too small, being only 3 in. long; the thickback because it is not abundant. The common sole is caught entirely by trawling, and off northwestern Europe around 34 000 tons are fished commercially each year, the most valuable grounds being in the central and southern North Sea and the Bay of Biscay. The name 'sole' has also been used for the lemon sole, which is a dab, and there is also the famous Dover sole. In the early 19th century a London merchant arranged for fast gigs to bring consignments of this fish post-haste from Dover, and the name has stuck for marketing the common sole, no matter where it comes from.

Deceitful sole

When dead the upper surface of the sole is a uniform sepia brown. In life most soles harmonize with the seabed on which they happen to be lying, their camouflage being helped by blotches, spots and bars, which further break up the outline of the body. The fact that a mature female lays over 500 000 eggs as compared with millions recorded for other fishes is a good indication that soles enjoy a fair measure of immunity from attack. One feature that may help is a black patch on the sole's pectoral fin. The poisonous weever fish, which also buries itself in the sand, has a black patch on its dorsal fin which it raises when a predator approaches. This is probably a warning signal to attackers that the fish is poisonous. The sole also raises its fin with a black patch and it has been suggested that this is a case of mimicry, the sole benefiting from being mistaken for a weever.

class	**Pisces**
order	**Pleuronectiformes**
family	**Soleidae**
genera & species	***Buglossidium luteum*** *solenette*
	Gymnarchirus williamsoni *naked sole*
	Microchirus variegatus *thickback sole*
	Pegusa lascaris *sand sole*
	Solea solea *common or Dover sole*

◁ *An alternating pattern: the comb-like ctenoid scales of the common sole (×34).*
▽ *A metamorphosising common sole, showing eye migration. In all soles the left eye migrates over to the right side of the body (×16).*

Denys A Kempson

DP Wilson

Solenodon

The two species of solenodon were first discovered by Europeans in 1833 on the islands of Hispaniola and Cuba. They are shrew-like creatures with an even more antiquated look about them than the true shrews. Fossil evidence shows that they were in existence 30 million years ago in North America. They seem therefore to be primitive insectivores—survivors from the past that have managed to hang on in these two islands because there are so few natural enemies there.

Solenodons are a foot long, with a tail up to 10 in. They have stout bodies with a disproportionately large head, made to look the more ungainly because of the unusually long snout. In most animals the snout forms a cushion of flesh just in front of the tips of the nasal bones. In solenodon, as in some other insectivores, there is a rod of cartilage, or gristle, in front of the nasals, supporting its unusually long snout. There are many long bristles on the face, the eyes are very small, the ears partly naked and mostly hidden in the fur. The coat is blackish to reddish brown, paler on the underside. The tail is nearly naked and so are the legs and the large feet each with five toes bearing large, strong claws. The especially large forefeet have larger and more curved claws than those on the hindfeet.

No straight path

One reason why it was so long before scientists got to know of solenodons is that they are nocturnal. They are also not very numerous. During the day they lie up in burrows, in hollow trees and logs or in caves, well out of sight. When they do come out they run on their toes with a stiff ungainly waddle, following an erratic almost zigzag course. The local people claim that solenodons never run in a straight line. Moreover, when a solenodon is alarmed and tries to put on speed it is as likely as not to trip over its own toes or even tumble head-over-heels. Like some of the shrews which they resemble, although they are not closely related to them, they have a poisonous saliva. The second incisor on each side in the lower jaw is grooved. Indeed, solenodon means grooved tooth. At the base of each of these incisors is a gland from which the poison runs along the groove in each tooth. When solenodons fight in captivity the light wounds inflicted are fatal.

Dying out in the midst of plenty

Solenodons eat a wide variety of animal and plant foods, such as insects, worms and small invertebrates generally, as well as small reptiles. They also eat roots, fruits and leaves. They root in the ground with their long snouts, dig with their stout claws or rip open rotten logs. Solenodons in captivity have been seen to bathe often and to drink only when bathing. Perhaps the long snout makes any other way difficult. For animals with such habits there is no shortage of food but solenodons are becoming more and more rare. This is partly

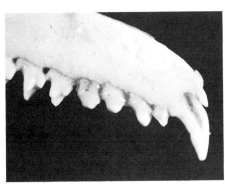

△ *Solenodon skull showing grooved second incisor down which the poisonous saliva flows.*
▽ *Haitian solenodon; this primitive insectivore is still present in areas of stony forest in the northeastern area of Haiti.*

due to their slow rate of breeding. The female may have two litters a year of 1–3 young but she has only two teats in an unusual position—almost on the buttocks!

Doomed

As well as having a poisonous bite a solenodon has glands in the armpits and in the groin, which give off a goat-like smell. It readily defends itself against one of its own kind, and probably attacks other animals savagely judging from the way a captive solenodon attacked a young chicken and tore it to pieces with its strong claws, before eating it. In moments of excitement it may grunt like a pig or give bird-like cries, but when pursued it stays motionless and hides its head, so it can be picked up easily. Taking all these facts together the solenodon is a slow mover, clumsy runner, with no agility in avoiding enemies and poor means of defence. As a result, once dogs and cats were taken to its island homes, and especially when mongooses were introduced, its future began to look black. Probably the only way of saving it would be to set up reserves, but this is hardly practical on Cuba or Hispaniola today, and tomorrow may be too late. Although we speak about what solenodons in captivity have done, these are only random observations and the number of animals that have found their way to zoos is very small: at the last count in June 1969 10 Haitian solenodons were to be found in 5 zoos throughout the world. No Cuban ones are in captivity as far as is known.

class	**Mammalia**
order	**Insectivora**
family	**Solenodontidae**
genus & species	***Solenodon cubanus*** *Cuban solenodon* **S. paradoxus** *Haitian solenodon*

Solifugid

These relatives of spiders probably have the strongest jaws, in proportion to their size, of any animals. Perhaps it is because they have so many names, such as false spiders, sun spiders, wind scorpions and camel spiders, that zoologists usually refer to them collectively as solifugids. There are also zoologists who speak of them as solpugids because the order to which they belong is variously known as the Solifugae or the Solpugida. This question of classification is relatively unimportant because they are fairly unknown.

Solifugids look like hairy spiders but differ from them in many ways. They seem to have very large heads because of the powerful jaws and the large muscles needed to work them. The thorax consists of three separate segments and the abdomen is also segmented. They appear to have five pairs of legs but the first pair are pedipalps which are long, powerful and very hairy, and each has a sucker at the end, used in climbing smooth surfaces. The chelicerae are held high up while the animal is moving and are used to seize prey. Behind them are four pairs of walking legs, each ending in a sharp claw, but the first pair are normally held up off the ground, like antennae. The hind pair of legs each bear five racquet-shaped organs. These may be used to detect movements of their prey.

The 600 species of solifugids are usually yellow, brown, or sometimes black. A few have stripes along the body. They vary from $\frac{1}{2}$–2 in. in length, and the larger species span 6 in. with their legs. They are especially numerous in the desert regions of Africa and Arabia but are found as far east as India. In Europe they occur only in southeast Spain. In North America they are found in Florida, in the deserts of the southwest United States and around hot springs as far north as southwest Canada. They also live in Central America and in the coastal areas of northern and western South America.

Sand plough

The name solifugid means 'fleeing from the sun' and most of the species are nocturnal. There are the others, however, which earn the name of sun spiders (aranhos del sol in Spanish). They all run quickly and the diurnal solifugids have been described as looking like balls of thistledown blown over the sand as they run about, hence the name wind scorpions. A solifugid will suddenly stop and quarter the ground as if it has sensed the presence of prey. Because they are so active solifugids need a more efficient breathing system, so instead of the lung books of spiders, they have a tracheal system like insects. When attacked they bend the abdomen up, recalling a scorpion's tail, but the solifugid does this only to keep its abdomen out of harm's way. The nocturnal

△ For its size the solifugid's chelicerae are massive. Each is composed of two parts which form a pair of strong pincer-like jaws that are used to kill the prey. ◁ Opposite: At the kill—G. arabs devours a young gecko. Solifugids have voracious appetites and will attack any small animal.

Aldo Margiocco

species hide under stones by day or bury in the sand, using their stout jaws to plough into the sand or scraping the sand backwards with their second pair of legs.

The female is more aggressive than the male towards other animals of their own size. The male will run from a scorpion, dodging the stabs from its sting. A female will attack, seizing the scorpion by the tail just behind the sting.

Real gluttons

Solifugids are wholly carnivorous. They eat insects, spiders, scorpions and smaller solifugids as well as small mice, birds and lizards. The prey is held and passed to and fro through the jaws by the pedipalps which chew it to a soft pulp. After this it sucks up the juices. A solifugid never drinks, probably because it gets all its moisture from its food. So long as there is food it will gorge itself until it can hardly move.

Fainting females

The males are lighter in colour, smaller, more active and have longer legs than the females. They also have narrower heads and smaller jaws, which may be why they flee, in contrast to the female which will stand her ground and fight. In courtship the male taps the female's body and strokes her, until she is in a trance-like state, when he can approach without danger of being attacked. The male then opens her genital orifice with one of the chelicerae, discharges a drop of sperm which he catches with the other chelicera and places inside the female. After this he scuttles away before she 'comes to'. The female goes into a deep burrow to lay her eggs, and stays beside them until they hatch. She then goes out to hunt for food for her offspring which she feeds until they are old enough to leave the burrow.

Biblical mice

Where solifugids are numerous there is a general belief that they are venomous. The fact is they produce no poison although they can inflict painful bites with their powerful jaws. These are normally reserved for their prey but sometimes people are bitten and one species living in parts of the North African desert is said to inflict particularly painful bites. JL Cloudsley-Thompson tells us that the Egyptians believe solifugids 'crawl in one's bed at night, bore into the crutch and lay their eggs'. The people of Baku, on the Caspian Sea, believe the local solifugids to be especially poisonous when they first come out of hibernation in the spring. The cure is to rub the wound with another solifugid—after steeping it in boiling oil—to neutralize the effects of the venom. It has been suggested, according to Cloudsley-Thompson, that the Hebrew word translated as 'mouse' in the Old Testament refers to some form of Solpuga, and that the sores from which the Philistines suffered were from their bites. He adds that their rapid movements and hairy bodies give an illusion of mice and 'they have been known to attack travellers asleep in the desert at night'.

phylum	**Arthropoda**
class	**Arachnida**
order	**Solifugae**
genera & species	*Galeodes arabs* *Rhagodessa cloudsley-thompsoni* others

Prepared for landing; a white throated sparrow
Zonotrichia albicollis, *a North American relative of the better known song sparrow.*

Song sparrow

A large number of finches living in North America are called sparrows. These include the grasshopper sparrow with its grasshopper-like buzz, the lark sparrow of the fields, the chipping sparrow of gardens and many others. At one time the song sparrow was just one of many similar birds, and very little was known about its habits. Then in 1937, Margaret Morse Nice published the results of an eight-year study of this familiar garden bird and it is now one of the best known of birds in North America.

Song sparrows look rather like house sparrows, about the same size, 5½ in. long, but without the black bib. Like many of their relatives they have whitish breasts with brown streaks running from the chin to the belly, but song sparrows are distinguished by the streaks converging to a conspicuous dark spot just below the throat. The plumage changes with the habitat, varying from pale in desert areas to dark in humid regions. Song sparrows in Alaska are much larger than those found elsewhere.

The range of the song sparrow is from Alaska and Canada, roughly on a line running through the southern shore of Hudson Bay, to the middle of the United States. It is more common in the east than in the drier west. In winter most song sparrows migrate southwards to the southern United States and Central America.

Persistent songster

The song sparrow has been divided into a number of races, each of which lives in a particular habitat, such as salt marsh, desert or meadow. It is, however, best known as a garden bird with a pleasant, lively song that can be heard for most of the year. Song sparrows may join in loose flocks during hard weather but by the end of winter they take up their territories and singing may start as early as late January. Singing can be heard until the end of the nesting season except, strangely enough, during the initial courtship. The main song period is in March when the males have established their territories but before their mates have joined them. Even immature males sing; they have a soft warble, unlike the song of the adult, but this changes to the adult song as soon as they start to show territorial behaviour.

They eat mainly seeds and insects, but also a few berries, snails and spiders. In summer about half their food is insects.

Large families

The outburst of singing in spring is a means of advertising to other male song sparrows that an area is already owned. When necessary singing is reinforced by fighting. Courtship is just as violent; the aggressive male pounces on any female that enters his territory and collides with her. If seriously looking for a mate, the female withstands these assaults and the male accepts and courts her. The female then builds a nest, the male carrying only a few symbolic beakfuls of nest material. The nest is made of dead grass and twigs and is lined with dried grass. Each pair of song sparrows may raise three broods of chicks, making a new nest for each. At the beginning of the nesting season, when the branches are bare, most nests are built on the ground, where they are concealed by herbage. Later nests are built above the ground among the foliage.

The usual clutch is 4—5 blue or grey-green eggs with brown spots. They are incubated by the female alone for 12—13 days. Both parents feed the chicks which leave the nest after 10 days. They continue to be fed for another 3 weeks but the female gradually leaves them in the male's charge while she starts to build another nest for the next clutch of eggs.

Extra babies

The song sparrow is one of the main hosts of the cuckoo-like cowbird (p 542). Where Dr Nice studied song sparrows in Ohio, 34% of the nests contained the eggs or nestlings of cowbirds, and sometimes as many as 78% of the song sparrows' nests may be parasitised. The song sparrows are still able to rear their brood along with a cowbird chick, but on average they raise one less chick of their own.

Who is the foe?

Cowbirds are not the only enemies of song sparrows and Dr Nice investigated the reactions of song sparrows to different predators. She found that song sparrows have separate calls and postures to indicate alarm, fear and fright and tested the reactions of captive song sparrows to live predators and models. In the wild, cats arouse alarm but hand-raised song sparrows ignore them. Owls evoke fear in nature and model owls alarm captive adults. Hand-raised chicks ignore them until 3 weeks old and then show alarm. These and other observations suggest that owls are recognised instinctively while the birds have to learn that cats are dangerous. It seems that memory and experience play a very important part in the recognition of enemies. Unpleasant experiences enhance fear, otherwise reactions wane. This explains, perhaps, why young birds so easily fall prey to enemies.

class	**Aves**
order	**Passeriformes**
family	**Fringillidae**
genus & species	***Melospiza melodia***

A closer look at the inconspicuous song sparrow reveals its finely patterned plumage.

Heinz Schrempp

South American deer

South American deer are small to medium-sized deer, the smallest standing only 16 in. at the shoulder. As is the case with so many South American animals, little is known of the 16 species of these extremely shy deer which remain under cover for most of the day, so are seldom seen. They belong to five different genera which have been grouped together here for convenience, under the single heading of South American deer.

Marsh deer

The marsh deer, sometimes called swamp deer, is the largest of the South American deer. It is 5 ft long in head and body, stands 40 in. at the shoulder and weighs 220 lb. Its coat is coarse and long, bright chestnut in summer and brownish-red in winter. The lower legs are black, the tail is yellowish red above and black below. The full grown antlers are doubly forked giving a total of four points. The hoofs can be spread widely, an adaptation to walking on soft ground.

The single species of swamp deer lives in Brazil, Paraguay and Uruguay.

Extremely shy and wary, swamp deer keep under cover by day and come into open spaces at night to feed on grass and water plants. They move about in groups of up to half-a-dozen in the high grass of wet savannahs, along the damp edges of forests, along river banks and on wooded islands. The deer readily take to water, both to feed and to escape. Being so elusive little is known of their habits. It is said the males do not drop their antlers at any set season. This is hard to believe except that it is also reported that the fawns are born at various times of the year, suggesting that breeding may be in any month. There is usually a single fawn, born after a gestation period of about nine months.

Deer among pampas grass

Another closely related species of South American deer also has no fixed breeding season in part of its range. It is the pampas deer, slightly smaller than the swamp deer, with a reddish-brown to yellowish-grey coat, dark markings on the face and white underparts. The bucks are said to give out, from their foot glands, a strong disagreeable odour which can be smelt up to a mile away. Pampas deer live among tall pampas grass, on the dry plains, in pairs or small herds. As the tall grass is cleared for cultivation the deer are forced into the open and so become very wary. The range of the pampas deer goes farther south than that of the swamp deer, from Brazil to Patagonia. In the northerly parts of the range it seems to have no fixed breeding season, but farther south, on the Argentine plains, it is said to breed at the end of summer.

An interesting feature reported for the pampas deer is that when female and young are suddenly disturbed, the fawn, which has a spotted coat, runs away to cover while the mother stands motionless at first then limps away, as if using the trick, more familiar in ground-nesting birds, of feigning injury.

△ A young **P. pudu**. Extremely shy in the wild this species of deer is easily tamed when young.
▽ Profile of a male Andean deer **Hippocamelus antisensis**, with its antlers in velvet. The antlers of this species of deer are small and simple and usually only branch once, near the base.

Werner Stangenberg: WWF

HG Klos: West Berlin Zoo

Deer in the Andes

The guemals, or Andean deer, are stocky deer with short stout legs. The males have short antlers which branch once near the base, the front prong being the smaller. About the same size as pampas deer, the guemal's coat is speckled yellow, grey and brown and there is a dark Y on the face. Both sexes have, like the Chinese water deer, long tusk-like canines but these do not hang low enough to be seen when the mouth is shut. The guemals are like pampas and swamp deer in habits except that they live at high altitudes in the Andes, in the forests or on grassy slopes, at 10–15 000 ft. They feed mainly on lichens and mosses and move down the mountainside into the valleys for the winter.

Spike-horned deer

The most numerous species of South American deer are the brockets. The four species are distributed from the Guianas across Brazil to the Andes, as well as south to Paraguay and northwards through Central America into Mexico. They are small, standing only 2 ft at the shoulder and weighing up to 46 lb. They have fox-red coats and short unbranched antlers, like the antlers of a red deer brocket, or first-year stag—hence the English name for this South American deer. A peculiarity of brockets is that they are high in the hindquarters.

Brockets are solitary or go about in pairs, feeding in the early morning and again at dusk, on grass and green shoots. They are extremely shy and secretive. Brockets are protectively coloured and freeze when alarmed. Breeding takes place throughout the year, with one spotted fawn at a birth.

Smallest American deer

The two species of pudu are the smallest American deer. One species *Pudu pudu*, ranging from central Chile almost to the Straits of Magellan, is up to 2 ft 8 in. long with an inch of tail, up to 16 in. high at the shoulder and weighs 20 lb. *P. mephistopheles* of Ecuador and Colombia is smaller, lives at higher altitudes of 9–12 000 ft, and has a richer brown coat than the pudu. Both species have short, spike-like antlers and narrow, pointed hoofs. They are not often seen, except when hunted with dogs. The fawns have three rows of white spots from the shoulder to the tail.

Few enemies

South American deer are preyed upon, although not heavily, by anacondas and boas, jaguars and pumas. The local people hunt them for their flesh and hides and because they damage crops. The antlers are valued for alleged medicinal purposes.

South American bounty

So little has been written about South American deer and they are so seldom photographed or kept in zoos, that even the informed zoologist carries away the impression that there can be few deer in

The small Andean deer, yellowish-grey-brown in colour, is recognized by the distinct black Y-shaped streak on the face.

South America. While it is true they do not form large herds, are probably less numerous in their populations and do not attain the sizes of deer elsewhere, South American deer are by no means as insignificant as they would appear. There are fewer than 50 species of deer in the world. Of these nearly 20 are from southern and southeast Asia and 16 from South America, a total greater than that for most of Asia, the whole of Europe and North America put together.

class	**Mammalia**
order	**Artiodactyla**
family	**Cervidae**
genera & species	***Blastocerus dichotomus*** *swamp deer* ***Ozotoceros bezoarticus*** *pampas deer* ***Hippocamelus*** *spp guemals* ***Mazama*** *spp brockets* ***Pudu*** *spp pudu*

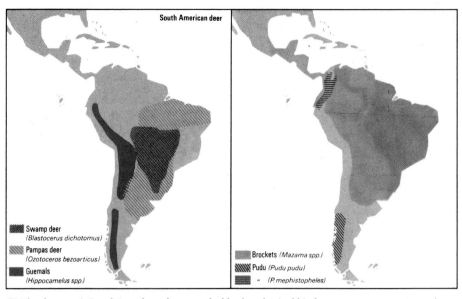

South American deer

Swamp deer *(Blastocerus dichotomus)*
Pampas deer *(Ozotoceros bezoarticus)*
Guemals *(Hippocamelus spp.)*

Brockets *(Mazama spp.)*
Pudu *(Pudu pudu)*
" *(P. mephistopheles)*

▽ *The characteristic red-fox coloured coat, arched back and raised hindquarters are very apparent in this* **Mazama americana.** *It is very shy, spending most of its time skulking in the undergrowth.*

Spadefoot

The spadefoot toads are named after the spade-like horny projection on the side of each hindfoot, with which they dig their burrows. The family of spadefoots is widely distributed over Europe, North Africa, southern Asia and North America. They are usually 3—4 in. long with a soft skin which is moist like that of a common frog rather than dry and warty like that of a common toad. The colour of the skin varies greatly between species. It may be grey, brown or green with red, white or black markings. There is also some variation in markings between the individuals of one species.

The European spadefoot is found over much of Europe south of southern Sweden and extends into Asia as far as Iran. Another European species is the mud-diver of southwestern Europe. In Asia there are the horned frogs which have three pointed projections of skin on the head, one on the snout and one above each eye. The best known spadefoots live in North America. They are related to the European spadefoot.

Spicy toads

Spadefoots are nocturnal, spending the day in burrows which they excavate by digging themselves in backwards with their spade-like hind legs. As they disappear beneath the surface the entrance of the burrow caves in so concealing it. The burrowing and nocturnal habits of spadefoots mean that they are often overlooked when they may be quite abundant, except during the breeding season when the males can be

▽ *Backward bulldozer: American spadefoot toad* **Scaphiopus intermontanus** *from the Great Basin of Nevada. The horny 'blade' used to burrow in reverse shows clearly on the hindfoot.*

John Tashjian

2157

△ *An apprehensive European spadefoot prepares to slam an earthy front door on the world by retreating to its burrow, the entrance of which will collapse.*

heard calling. Spadefoots are mainly found in sandy areas where burrows are easy to dig. In dry weather they may burrow 6 – 7 ft down to find moist soil.

Some spadefoots give a shrill cry when handled, which may be a means of deterring predators. They may also give off secretions from glands in the skin. In certain species such as the Mexican spadefoot small glands give off an unpleasant tasting secretion that also irritates the lining of the nose and mouth. The European spadefoot is called the *Knoblauchskrote,* or garlic toad, in Germany because the secretions from its skin smell rather like garlic.

The food of spadefoots is insects and other small invertebrates.

Growing up together

The general breeding pattern of the spadefoot is not very different from that of the common toad. In spring the males of the European spadefoot, for example, resort to ponds where they call, attracting the females to them. Their eggs are laid in gelatinous strings among the stems of water plants. The tadpoles hatch out about 5 days later and, at first, lack both gills and tail, and measure only ⅛ in. External gills and tail grow within a day or so and development continues normally, with the external gills being replaced by internal gills and the legs growing, until the tadpoles are 4 in. long. The tail is then resorbed and the resulting toadlets leave the pond.

A variation of this pattern is seen in an Asian species in which courtship takes place on land and the pairs then go to a stream for egg-laying. Among the North American spadefoots there are, however, some very remarkable habits. These toads live in the dry parts of the southwestern United States

and breed when shallow ponds are temporarily filled with rainwater. They have, therefore, to start breeding as soon as the ponds fill and their offspring have to be independent before they dry up again.

A brief adolescence

Shortly after a storm the males of these spadefoots search for water and when they have found a suitable stretch of standing water they start to call. Their calls attract other males so a chorus builds up that eventually attracts the females and pairs form for mating. The louder the chorus from any pond, the more females are attracted to it, which is an efficient way of ensuring rapid pairing. The eggs hatch in 2 days, a much shorter time than that known for any other frog or toad. The tadpoles grow very rapidly but sometimes the temporary pools dry up before they can change into toadlets. In some species the tadpoles gather in compact groups if the water level is dangerously low and wriggle together to form a depression in the mud where the remaining water can collect. The tadpoles change into toadlets by the resorbtion of the tail in half an hour. They gather at the water's edge in masses and they all leave together, so overnight the pond loses all its tadpoles.

When there is a shortage of food in a pool the tadpoles band together and move over the bottom, stirring it with their tails to expose food. The tadpoles also eat the bodies of other tadpoles that have died from starvation. This means that in bad conditions a few survive instead of all of them dying. It has also been found that when a pond is drying up tadpoles which have fed on other tadpoles complete their development more rapidly, so increasing the chances of the strongest youngsters' survival.

Each to his own

In the western United States there are four species of spadefoot which are very similar but only rarely interbreed. Where two or more live in the same place, interbreeding is prevented by females only responding to the calls of males of their own species and by the slightly different habits of different spadefoot species. Thus Hunter's and Couch's spadefoots breed in the shallows while the plains and Hammond's spadefoots prefer deeper water.

There is also a great difference in the kinds of soil in which the American spadefoots prefer to live and this also results in the species being kept apart. In Texas Hunter's spadefoot likes sandy areas whereas Couch's spadefoot prefers soil which is not sandy. This is a sufficient barrier to keep them apart, except where man has disturbed the soil. At one place disturbed ground supports both species, and they interbreed occasionally.

class	**Amphibia**
order	**Salientia**
family	**Pelobatidae**
genera & species	***Megophrys nasuta*** *horned frog*
	Pelobates fuscus
	European spadefoot
	Pelodytes punctatus *mud-diver*
	Scaphiopus bombifrons
	plains spadefoot
	S. *couchi* *Couch's spadefoot*
	S. *hammondii*
	Hammond's spadefoot
	S. *holbrookii*
	Hunter's or eastern spadefoot
	S. *multiplicatus* *Mexican spadefoot*

Sparrow

The name 'sparrow' is given to a number of birds including the North American song sparrow (p 2208) and its relatives. True sparrows belong to the genus **Passer**, the Latin word for sparrow and from which the vast order of perching birds or Passeriformes gets its name. Closely related to the true sparrows are the rock sparrows and snow-finches. Together with the sparrow-weavers they make up the subfamily Passerinae which is related to the true weavers such as the bishopbirds (p 209), fodis (p 808), and queleas (p 1882).

The best known sparrow is the house sparrow which has become completely dependent on man and has been spread by him to many parts of the world. About 5¾ in. long, the male has brown upperparts with black streaks, greyish underparts, a black bib, white bars on the wings and a grey rump which can be seen in flight. The female is duller and lacks the bib, the wing bar and the grey rump. Three closely related sparrows can be confused with the house sparrow. The Spanish sparrow of Spain, Italy, Greece and North Africa can be distinguished by a generally darker plumage with the black bib extending onto the breasts and sides and a brown rather than a grey crown. The Italian sparrow, restricted to Italy and Corsica, is intermediate between the house and Spanish sparrows, having a dark brown crown but a restricted black bib. The tree sparrow has a dark brown crown and a black spot on the whitish cheeks. It breeds in Europe and Asia, from the British Isles to Japan. The desert sparrow lives in the deserts of Africa and Asia. The rock sparrows live mainly in Africa, with three species extending into Asia and one into Europe. The snow-finches are found in mountains from the Pyrenees to Mongolia.

Community life

House sparrows live in flocks with a strong bond between the members. They feed, dust-bathe and roost together and when one gives the alarm they fly to cover in a tight bunch. The members of a flock communicate by means of simple calls—the familiar chirruping and cheeping. The call is basically a means of identification and keeps the flock together as they go about their activities or merely perch doing nothing. This is particularly so when a flock gathers in a tree prior to flying to their roost. In London the places where these chattering masses gathered were once called 'sparrows' chapels'. The call is also used by the male sparrow as a song to proclaim the ownership of his nest site and to attract a mate, while variations are used to give alarm.

Mainly grain eaters

Sparrows are seed eaters, and the house sparrow specialises on grain. When they occur in large numbers they often become pests because a flock can strip a seed crop, and beat down the stems in a very short time. Numerous campaigns have been mounted against house sparrows, the most spectacular being that in China which involved the mobilisation of the human population. There has, however, been little success in eliminating these birds. They are very adaptable, being able to feed on all sorts of food such as kitchen scraps and other refuse, while in the days of horse-drawn traffic, urban house sparrows lived largely on spillings from nosebags and undigested grains from droppings.

The natural food of house sparrows includes insects, worms, buds and fruit. They also gather food in the same ways as several other birds; they fly out after insects from perches in the same way as flycatchers, hover and pounce like kestrels, search

▽ Cold and probably hungry, a cock (left) and a hen house sparrow; many sparrows rely entirely on man's scraps for food at this time of year.

leaves like tits and flutter after low-flying insects like wagtails. The habit of tearing up flowers, particularly yellow ones, has not yet been explained.

Wedding parties

The true sparrows build domed nests of grass similar to those of other members of the family. The nests are usually built in a hole in a tree, in crevices in buildings or in the nests of other birds such as house martins. The Spanish sparrow nests in colonies with several hundreds of nests all built in a few trees and the chestnut sparrow nests in communities although it does not build its own nests; it takes over nests in the huge communal structures built by the social weavers.

House sparrows are found near their nest holes for most of the year and in winter they may roost in their nests. At the start of the breeding season the male advertises his nest site by chirruping and females are attracted to inspect the site. There is little ceremony in courtship but there is a peculiar activity called the 'sparrows' wedding' or 'sparrows' party' in which a twittering party of males chase a female, who may

turn on the males and attack them. Mating does not take place and the significance of this activity is not known.

Both sexes build the nest and line it with feathers and both incubate the clutch of whitish, brown-mottled eggs. The clutch usually numbers 2–4 in the tropics and 3–7 in cooler parts. The chicks leave the nest in about a fortnight and there may be 3–4 broods in one year.

Man's constant companion

The house sparrow is unique among birds as it lives only in man-made habitats. It is presumed that it evolved from the Spanish sparrow because, although they are separate in Europe, they interbreed in North Africa. The tree sparrow also lives with man in some places, but where the house sparrow is spreading, such as in India, it is driving the tree sparrow out of the towns. Part of the house sparrow's success must be due to its wide range of feeding habits, especially its preference for grain, and its ability to nest on houses. This allows it to nest in the very

centre of cities and in big warehouses it is possible that the house sparrows pass their whole lives without venturing into the open.

Being so adaptable the house sparrow has followed Europeans as they spread to new continents and it is now abundant in North and South America, South Africa, Australia and New Zealand. Incredibly, considering that it is often a pest, the house sparrow was deliberately introduced in some places. It was even protected by law at first and only later were these laws rescinded and replaced by bounty schemes, by which time it was too late to stop the spread.

class	**Aves**
order	**Passeriformes**
family	**Ploceidae**
genus & species	*Passer domesticus* house sparrow *P. d. italiae* Italian sparrow *P. eminebey* chestnut sparrow *P. hispaniolensis* Spanish sparrow *P. montanus* tree sparrow *P. simplex* desert sparrow others

Crop raid: a mixed flock of tree and house sparrows descends on a cereal field; in a matter of hours they will have stripped or ruined most of it.

Arne Schmitz: Photo Res

André Fatras

△ *The next generation: sparrowhawk in juvenile plumage. Whether or not it, in turn, will breed, depends on the amount of persistent insecticide it has consumed.*

▷ *A sparrowhawk stands guard over its brood —the bundles of white fluff in the nest.*

Sparrowhawk

*Many hawks in the genus **Accipiter**, to which the goshawks also belong, are called sparrowhawks, but the sparrowhawk of Europe, Africa and Asia is one of the best studied birds of prey. Many of the other sparrowhawks live in southeast Asia, particularly on the numerous islands, or in Africa and their habits are not at all well known. In America, the kestrel **Falco sparverius** is called a sparrowhawk.*

The sparrowhawks are considerably different in appearance from the falcons. They have short rounded wings and fly with alternate bursts of rapid wingbeats and long glides. Sparrowhawks vary in length from 11—15 in., the female being considerably larger than the male. The male is dark above with finely barred red-brown underparts and a whitish chin. The female is darker above but has white underparts with a little brown barring. Both have whitish napes, barred tails and long legs.

The sparrowhawk breeds in most of Europe except the treeless north, and northwest Africa. In Asia it lives in Iran and the Himalayas, and east to Kamchatka.

Victim of DDT

Sparrowhawks live in woods and forests or in open places where there are a few trees. Even where abundant they are not seen as frequently as the kestrel because they spend most of their time in cover and typically hunt by flying behind hedges or through trees to take their prey unawares. Sparrowhawks are not, however, shy birds and have been known to fly into houses after their prey. Presumably the small birds, which are their main prey, take refuge in houses as a substitute for dashing into the cover of foliage, their usual place of safety.

RK Murton: Photo Res

2161

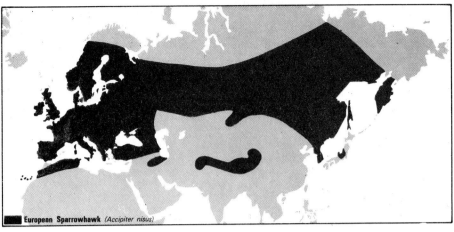

European Sparrowhawk (*Accipiter nisus*)

The presence of sparrowhawks may be given away by the pellets, feathers and bones of their prey which accumulate around regular feeding posts. At one time sparrowhawks were very common in agricultural areas where there were sufficient trees to provide cover but with the introduction of DDT and other long lasting insecticides there was a serious decline in sparrowhawk numbers. This has not received the publicity that the plight of the peregrine and the golden eagle has received yet sparrowhawks have probably been harder hit, possibly because they live largely in agricultural areas and hunt birds that feed on dressed seed.

Sparrowhawks that breed in northern regions migrate south in winter. North European sparrowhawks cross the Bosphorus and Gibraltar to winter in Africa.

Sudden death to prey

The hunting habits of the sparrowhawk are as characteristic as those of the kestrel. It takes its prey by surprise, swooping on an unsuspecting animal and killing it with its long sharp claws. Sometimes a sparrowhawk flips upside down and strikes its prey from underneath. Most prey is caught completely unawares as the sparrowhawk glides rapidly along the edge of a wood or quarters a hedge by suddenly darting from one side to the other, but occasionally small birds are pursued through the air and out-paced.

To anyone who sees a small bird suddenly disappear as a sparrowhawk flashes past, this method of hunting must seem breathtakingly efficient. It has been shown, however, that the sparrowhawk is successful in only one out of 10 attempts at a kill and when it is successful the prey is probably sick or already wounded.

The main prey of sparrowhawks is small birds such as sparrows, finches, tits and robins but each of these birds is very small and an equal weight of larger birds, up to the size of wood pigeons, is taken. Birds make up about $\frac{2}{3}$ of the diet, insects about $\frac{1}{5}$, and the remainder consists of reptiles, amphibia and small mammals up to the size of a rabbit.

Young birds practise hunting

The courtship of sparrowhawks is similar to that of other birds of prey, with both partners taking part in aerial chases and fights, the male sometimes swooping at the female. Unlike the falcons, sparrowhawks build their own nests, constructing loose piles of

interwoven twigs which are lined with green leaves. The female does most of the building but the male gathers much of the material and also feeds the female. He also feeds her while she incubates the clutch of 2–7 eggs. The chicks hatch out after an incubation of 5 weeks but they are brooded by the female for another week. She does not, however, help the male in hunting until the chicks are 3 weeks old. The chicks first fly when just over 1 month old but cannot kill their own food for another week or more. They begin by catching insects as more practice is needed before birds can be caught.

Sparrowhawks control sparrows

At one time sparrowhawks were persecuted, like other birds of prey, because of damage done to game birds and poultry. The number of these birds that they do in fact kill is small and it is now realised that sparrowhawks are on the whole useful. In one sample of sparrowhawk prey it was found that about 60% of the animals killed were detrimental to man's interests and many of the small birds that sparrowhawks kill are grain eaters. Such information is now turning the tide of opinion in favour of predators, both among birds and other animals. In Holland, for instance, nest boxes are put out to encourage kestrels which help control the numbers of rodents.

Sparrows are the birds most frequently killed by sparrowhawks and it seems that sparrowhawks, if reasonably abundant, can control the numbers of this grain-eating bird. Sparrowhawks are indeed well named and they were used in one of the first attempts at biological control. In 1851 the Crystal Palace was the centrepiece of an International Exhibition held in London. Sparrows got into the vast glass building and became a nuisance. Queen Victoria sought the advice of the Duke of Wellington and this statesman's advice was terse and to the point: 'Sparrowhawks, Ma'am.'

class	**Aves**
order	**Falconiformes**
family	**Accipitridae**
genus & species	***Accipiter nisus***

Heinz Schrempp

Born to kill: a sparrowhawk flexes its wings in anticipation of a foray. It hunts small birds by surprise attack, stealing along hedgerows and wood fringes and pouncing with long, out-stretched talons on any small birds it happens to flush. Falconers usually make little use of sparrowhawks: they prefer more accurate and spectacular birds of prey, like the gyrfalcon.

Spectacled bear

The single species of spectacled bear, sometimes called the Andean bear, is found in tropical South America and is the only South American bear. It is one of the smaller bears, 5 – 6 ft long with a small tail of 2 – 3 in. and standing only about 30 in. at the shoulder. A full-grown male may weigh up to 300 lb. The shaggy coat is black or blackish-brown with large circles or semi-circles of white or buff around the eyes which gives the animal its common name. The muzzle is the same colour and there is a white patch on the neck which extends in uneven streaks onto the chest. The head and chest markings vary considerably in different animals and may sometimes be entirely lacking. The coat is much less thick than that of bears from temperate climates.

The spectacled bear lives in the forests in the foothills of the Andes up to an altitude of 10 000 ft in western Venezuela, Colombia, Ecuador, Peru and western Bolivia and possibly in Panama. Although it usually keeps to the forested areas it sometimes ranges into the higher clearings or into the plains, savannahs and scrublands at quite low altitudes.

Little known of habits

Very little is known of the habits of the spectacled bear. Like most bears it is an expert climber and will climb trees to a height of as much as 80 – 100 ft, in search of food. It is strong for its size and is reputed to be able to break saplings 3 in. in diameter. It is reported to make large nests of sticks in the trees and although this has never been confirmed it is quite possible since there are other small bears that do so.

Mostly vegetarian

Unlike most bears the spectacled bear is thought to feed largely on leaves, fruits and roots although in captivity some will take a certain amount of meat and there have been reports of wild bears preying on deer, guanacos and vicuñas. In Ecuador it feeds largely on the pambili palm, climbing the tree and tearing off branches, the leaves of which are eaten later on the ground. It will also tear open the green stalks of young palms to reach the tender pith inside and will also eat the buds. In northern Peru it feeds on the fruits of a species of *Capparis*.

Breeding in zoos

The breeding habits of the spectacled bear are known only from the few animals that have been kept in zoos. Nothing is known of them in the wild. Records dated 1951 concerning a well-established colony in the Zoological Gardens of Buenos Aires give the gestation period as 8 – 8½ months, the number of young as 1 or 2 and the times of birth as June, July and September. The Zoological Gardens of Basle reported that a pregnant female received by them from a dealer on November 25 1952 gave birth to 3 cubs on February 17 1953.

Spectacled bears in captivity

The spectacled bear has never been numerous in zoos probably because of the inaccessibility of its natural habitat. The Zoological Gardens of London had their first specimen in 1832. An animal that arrived at the New York Zoological Society in 1909 was thought to be the first to be seen alive in the United States. At first spectacled bears did not survive for long in captivity until it was realised that their diet was nearly wholly vegetarian. When this was provided they lived much longer. One large male was kept for 16 years in the New York Zoological Park from November 1940 until June 1957. It was kept in an outside den that was snug but unheated and it was found to be quite hardy at that latitude. Although in a much colder climate than that of its natural habitat it showed no inclination to become dormant during the winter, however bad the weather. Its daily diet consisted of one quart of reconstituted evaporated milk, 18 apples and 7 loaves of raisin bread. It never accepted meat or even a mixture of chopped meat and dog meal, although a young one the Zoo had later, accepted small quantities of both.

The longest living captive spectacled bear was one in the San Diego Zoological Gardens which lived for over 21 years.

Not so spectacled

The spectacled bear is an excellent example of something the experienced zoologist takes for granted but is not generally realized by the non-zoologist: that is, that animals vary in their physical characters just as people do. This variation is more pronounced in some species than others, but it is always there. The spectacled bear, as we have said, is named for the white rings around its eyes. If, however, one only looked for these rings to identify the bear there would be disappointments. In addition to the white 'spectacles' there is usually a small amount of white on the snout. In some of these bears the white rings may be so enlarged and the white on the snout so extensive that the face becomes a white mask with just a little black round the eyes. At the other extreme all the white on the face may be lost and the bear is left with only a white muzzle. There are all gradations between these two extremes so in effect no two spectacled bears are alike in face.

class	**Mammalia**
order	**Carnivora**
family	**Ursidae**
genus & species	***Tremarctos ornatus***

▷ *Seven faces of spectacled bears. Although there is only one species of this bear, there are innumerable different facial markings.*
◁ *A spectacled bear draws itself up to its full height while a junior squats on its haunches. Its long shaggy coat is not as thick as that of bears from more temperate climates, for this bear comes from the tropics of South America. Most knowledge of its behaviour has been learned from those kept in zoos.*

Chris Howell-Jones after Dr S Raethal & Dr HH Roth

Sperm whale

The sperm whale is shaped like a gigantic tadpole, a third of its total length being taken up by its massive head. The body is thickest just behind the head, in what should be the neck region, and from there it tapers backwards to the tail flukes. Seen from the side the head looks squarish but from the front it is rounded above with a wide groove each side, and below this it curves inwards on either side to the upper jaw. The lower jaw is small in comparison with the rest of the head. It is Y-shaped, being wide at the angle of the mouth and narrowing rapidly so that the two halves run together towards the front. There are 18—28 conical teeth on each side of the lower jaw, each up to 8 in. long, and when the mouth is shut, these fit into sockets in the upper jaw which at the most has a few vestigial teeth. There is a single blowhole to the left on top of the head. The interior of the mouth and the tongue are pearly white. A sperm whale has no dorsal fin. Instead there is a series of half a dozen low humps or ridges along the rear third of the back. The greatest length recorded for a sperm whale is 84 ft, but males are usually up to 60 ft and the females are little more than half this length. The males weigh 33 tons on average, with a maximum of 53 tons, and the females weigh about 13 tons, with a maximum of 14 tons. Sperm whales are black or nearly so on the back, lighter on the flanks and silvery grey to white on the underside.

Although most common in the warmer seas, sperm whales are found throughout all oceans, including both north and south polar seas. The main stock is, however, found between latitudes 40 degrees north and south.

The two species of pygmy sperm whales, genus **Kogia**, are up to 12 ft long, and lack the massive barrel-like head of their relatives, being more dolphin-shaped.

Asleep over the deep

Sperm whales move about in schools or herds of mainly three kinds: harems made up of cows and calves and usually led by a dominant male; bachelor schools; and loose groups of lone bulls. There are occasional rogue bulls that are particularly aggressive, as in the tradition of Moby Dick. The harems especially keep within the latitudes of 40 degrees, which is why bulls only are found in temperate and polar seas. Usually all that is seen of sperm whales is the 'blow', or at most their backs, except when they breach—that is, leap clear of the water and fall back flat on the surface. They surface for 10 minutes at a time, take 60—70 breaths then submerge for anything up to an hour, going down almost vertically. Sperm whales are renowned for their deep dives—a whale is said to sound when it dives. The records are from cable ships hoisting broken submarine cables to the surface for repairs and finding a sperm whale tangled with the cable, usually by its lower jaw. The greatest depth recorded was 3 240 ft. Sometimes a sperm whale will 'lobtail', or stand on its head with the tail flukes 30 feet above the surface. It may then smack the surface with its tail with explosive force, the sound being audible for miles around.

▷ *Solitary bull sperm whale at speed on the surface, showing the typical offset blowhole.*
▷▷ *Massive head and jaw, showing tiny eye.*
▽▷ *Harpooned for its oil, a rare white sperm whale breaks the surface for the last time.*
▽ *A huge tooth from a sperm whale's lower jaw.*

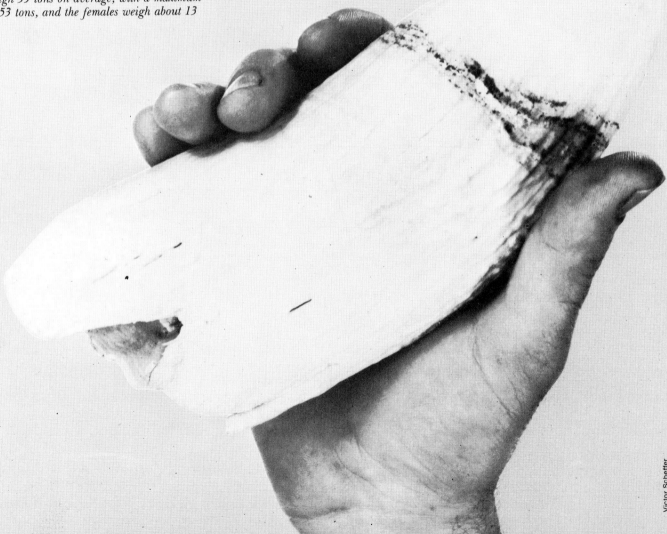

Ships, from merchant vessels to warships, have collided with sperm whales. In the Second World War, at night, an American destroyer felt a heavy jolt, rapidly lost speed, and the ship's company took to their boats under the impression they had been torpedoed. Next morning a sperm whale was found transfixed to the bows. There are a number of other such records and the assumption is that the whales are asleep when hit! That they are the deepest sleepers of all whales stems from this. They have been reported playing with floating planks, as when a ship passed a school, all of which swam away except one which repeatedly dived below the plank. This is interpreted as play related to the instinct of these whales to rescue a calf, for although a sperm whale will desert an injured mate it will, apparently, respond to the distress cries of a nursing calf. There are reports of the adult taking a calf in its mouth and rising to the surface with it.

Meals of giant squid

The main food of sperm whales is squid and cuttlefish, including giant squids, and scars on the whales' bodies, apart from those due to males fighting, are from the hooks and suckers of their prey. Some of the sucker marks are 4 in. across, telling of encounters with very large squid. Dr Robert Clarke found a squid 34 ft 5 in. long and weighing 405 lb in the stomach of a 47ft sperm whale harpooned off the Azores in July 1955. Harpooned sperm whales sometimes vomit the remains of squid and one was seen to give up 75−100 squid in this way, most of them being 3−4 ft long, the usual size of squid they take. They will also take seals and fish; one was found to have a 10ft shark in its stomach.

One calf every four years

Puberty occurs in the male when he is 39−40 ft long but he is not sexually mature until 45−46 ft long. The female matures sexually at about 28 ft long and her reproductive cycle lasts 4 years: 14½ months pregnancy, 24−25 months suckling a calf − there is usually only one at a birth − and a nine-month 'resting' period before breeding again. Most of our information comes from South Africa where there is a pairing season off Durban from October to April with a peak in December. After mating the females go north to spend the winter in equatorial waters, returning south in spring. The young males go with them, the mature bulls following later. The newly born young is 13 − 14 ft long.

Valuable ambergris

The sperm whale fishery began in the early 18th century and was mainly in the hands of American whalers from the New England coast. At its height it produced 4 million gallons of oil from the blubber, which may be as much as 14 in. thick. The fishery was finished by the end of the 19th century, partly because the stocks in the western Atlantic were seriously reduced but more especially because whale oil was replaced by mineral oil for lighting. There are still fisheries for sperm whales, off the Azores, off South Africa, in the Pacific and also, to a lesser extent, in a few other places. The more valuable part of the sperm whale was the large reservoir of spermaceti in the head. As much as 15 barrels could be tapped from one whale. This clear colourless oil solidifies to a soft white wax and is used in making candles, cosmetics, medicines, and for various other purposes such as dressing fabrics. The substance the sperm whale is most remembered for, however, is its ambergris. This is grey to black in colour, lighter than water, and smells offensively when fresh from the whale's intestine but later has a characteristic sweet earthy odour. Ambergris had a high value for medicinal purposes and as a base for the finest perfumes, although in fact it is only a by-product of the whale's digestion. It is still not certain why it should be formed but it almost certainly has something to do with the squid and cuttlefish eaten by the whale. Usually ambergris is found in small pieces floating on the sea. Occasionally masses weighing several hundred pounds are found in a whale's intestine when it is opened up on the flensing deck. In former times ambergris was literally worth its weight in gold, and the Dutch East India Company had a piece weighing 975 lb. At that time it was in demand for love philtres, among other things. In 1953 another mass weighing 918 lb was taken from a whale in the Antarctic − and even then the price, although it had dropped, was £70 per lb.

class	**Mammalia**
order	**Cetacea**
family	**Physeteridae**
genera & species	***Physeter catodon*** *sperm whale* ***Kogia spp.*** *pygmy sperm whales*

▽ *Industry on the high seas. Men put out in tiny rowing boats to harpoon the sperm whales. As well as for their oil, the whales were hunted for ambergris, a product of their digestion. It had a high medicinal value and was literally worth its weight in gold.*

Victor Scheffer

Spider crab

*The largest recorded crab measured 12½ ft across its outstretched claws. It was a specimen of **Macrocheira kaempferi**, the giant crab of Japan. In contrast to this enormous span, the body measured a mere 15 in. The weight of this crab is not known but one spanning a little over 12 ft weighed 41 lb. Another large spider crab **Leptomithrax spinulosus** is only up to 2½ ft across the extended claws and 6 in. across the back. It lives off the south-east coast of Australia. Many spider crabs are very small—like the long-beaked spider crab of Europe, **Macropodia rostrata**, with a shell less than ½ in. across. It is commonly found under stones and among weeds low on the shore and is the most spidery European species with its long slender hairy legs. The first of the four pairs of walking legs are the longest, being at least three times the length of the body. Its claws are shorter than its walking legs and are rather heavy in the male. The triangular or pear-shaped body, usually reddish in colour, narrows to the front where it ends in a pair of prongs between the stalked eyes. This two-pointed beak or rostrum at the front is typical of spider crabs. The surface of the body is variously spined or covered in warts depending on the species. The abdomen, or tail, tucked underneath as in other crabs, may be six- or seven-jointed.*

The biggest and best-known European species is the spiny spider crab or thornback crab. Although sometimes found low on the shore it is commoner in deeper water usually in 90–600 ft and is very abundant in some years, to the displeasure of lobster fishermen whose pots it infests. Though its body is 2–7 in. across, it is of little commercial value for there is little muscle in its small claws. Its legs are slender, but not particularly long. The body is generally reddish with pink, brown or even yellowish markings. About six hard spines project on either side of the shell and others cover the surface.

Usually lethargic

Spider crabs are generally slow moving scavengers, especially of dead flesh, relying more on concealment than speed for protection. The sluggishness of these and some other crabs is found to be linked with a high level of magnesium in their blood as compared with that in more active crustaceans; magnesium salts are well known for their anaesthetic action. There is always a tendency for salts in the body fluids of marine animals which become concentrated to be lost to the surrounding sea water when there are no physiological mechanisms to prevent it. The concentration of magnesium in the blood of spider crabs is much the same as that in sea water. Thus it would seem that the high levels of magnesium in these species reflect an inability to keep them lower. By comparison with, say, the

shore crab (p 2127), which can regulate the salt composition of its body fluids to some extent, the spider crab lacks this ability. This explains their inability to penetrate the brackish water of estuaries.

The kelp crab *Pugettia producta* is more active than most spider crabs and clings strongly to one's fingers if picked up. It is found on seaweed beaches on the Pacific coast from British Columbia to Lower California. It does not purposely adorn its carapace, but uninvited barnacles and anemones are often found clinging to it.

Heather Angel

△ European **Maia squinado** *curled for defence.* ▷ *Overleaf:* **Stenorhynchus seticornis.**

Four stages of crab

The life history of a spider crab is like that of other crabs, involving two zoea stages followed by a transformation into the more crab-like megalopa. The zoea larva has big eyes, a long abdomen and two large spines, one forming a downwardly-directed 'beak' and the other projecting upwards from the back. Moulting ceases at puberty.

Long legs, green fingers

There are many examples of camouflage in the animal kingdom. Some spider crabs tend to stay on the background they match, like *Parthenope investigatoris*, a spider crab of the Indian Ocean, which looks like a piece of the worn coral among which it lives. Others change colour to suit the background they happen to be on. Spider crabs include a number of species that camouflage themselves with seaweeds, sponges, hydroids, or moss animals, each piece plucked and fastened onto the body. A sticky secretion from the mouth is sometimes used to attach the fragments, but in many spider crabs the surface of the shell bears special hooked or serrated bristles or bundles of hairs that curl like tendrils around whatever is planted on them. Many of the smaller and commoner spider crabs cover their bodies in this way and *Camposcia retusa* of tropical reefs is called the harlequin crab for the assortment of gaily-coloured fragments it

places on its shell. By contrast *Inachus dorsettensis*, of the British Isles, a small yellowish-brown crab, camouflages only its first pair of walking legs. In the United States spider crabs are called, appropriately, decorator crabs. Camouflaging species tend to occur more in clear water than where visibility is poor. The garden is replaced each time the shell is moulted but a new one may be replanted in certain circumstances. Thus, when some spider crabs *Hyas*, covered with seaweed, were placed in an aquarium with sponges and no weed, they removed their inappropriate camouflage of weed and changed it for a new one of sponge. Denuded of all covering by the experimenter, they became very perturbed and uncharacteristically active.

A spider crab *Podochela hemphilli*, on the California coast, clothes itself with the more delicate red seaweeds and while it is stationary waves the weed back and forth by rocking its body, so adding to the realism. When hungry it eats pieces of its camouflage. This looks like an intelligent action, and the things spider crabs do often seem clever, but a spider crab which had the top of its brain removed, decorated itself with any suitable materials, such as scraps of paper, that it touched with its legs.

The large European *Maia squinado*, about a foot across, decorates its shell when young but gives up the habit as it grows larger—and better able to defend itself. *Loxorhynchus grandis* of the American Pacific coast starts to lose the instinct to camouflage itself when it is 3 in. across the shell. Fully grown it is 42 in. across the legs.

phylum	**Arthropoda**
class	**Crustacea**
subclass	**Malacostraca**
order	**Decapoda**
superfamily	**Oxyrhincha**

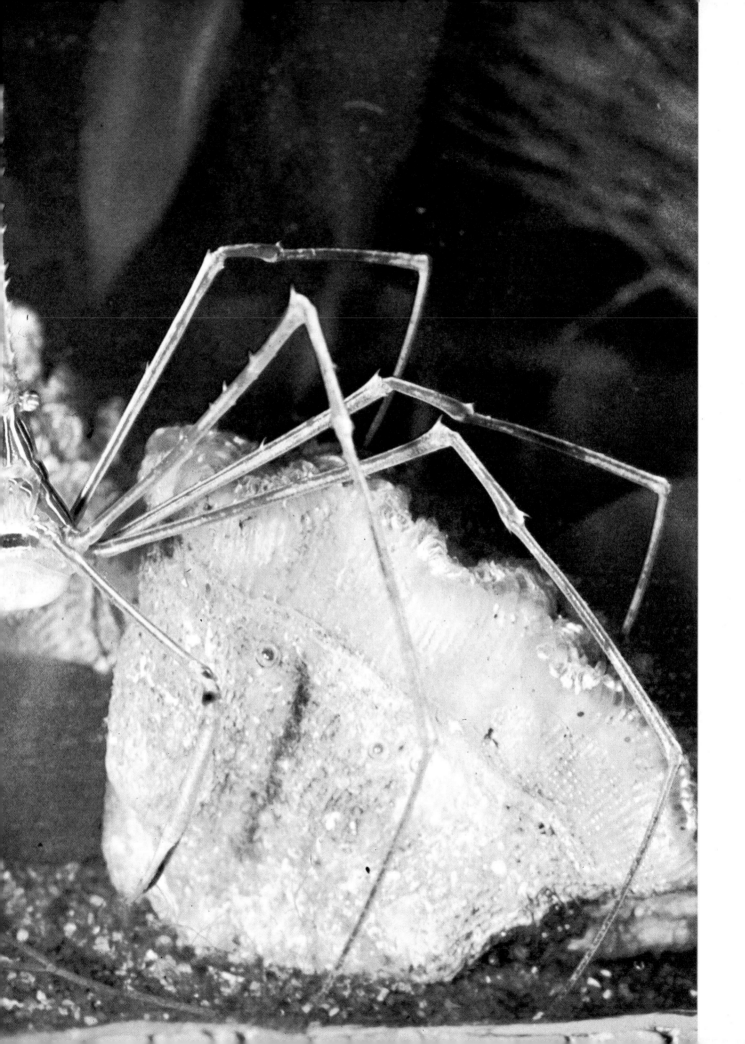

Spider monkey

Spider monkeys are among the best-known and most highly specialised of the South American monkeys. Like the others their noses have nostrils looking out to the sides with a very broad septum between. They also have three premolars in each half of each jaw unlike the African and Asian monkeys which have only two premolars. Their skull characters and anatomical details also make South American monkeys less like man than the Old World monkeys and apes, although in man the third molars, or wisdom teeth, are often missing.

Spider monkeys are slenderly built but pot-bellied. Their fur is usually rather wiry, and sparse on the underside. Their remarkably prehensile tail, which can wrap round and cling on to branches, has on the underside of its tip a completely hairless area, a few inches long, marked by wrinkles and ridges like fingerprints. These enable it to get a firmer grip. Their hands are modified as hooks, with long narrow palms, long curved fingers and no thumbs.

*There are two species. The common spider monkey has coarse wiry hair, and may be a variety of colours according to race, one race being black and buff, another wholly black and another is black with a red face and genitalia. The woolly spider monkey, from the dry hardwood forests of southeastern Brazil, has thicker, more woolly hair and is more robustly built. It is yellowish or greyish brown, rather darker on the head and neck. Because of its heavier build and the nature of its fur, it somewhat resembles a woolly monkey genus **Lagothrix**, and it used to be put into a separate genus, **Brachyteles**, but nowadays the resemblances are thought to be only superficial. It is heavier than the common spider monkey, being 21 lb as against 12–15 lb, but both species are much the same length, about 16–26 in. head and body, with 24–36 in. of tail. Woolly spider monkeys are rare today due to the cutting down of forests.*

Ape-like habits

Spider monkeys are very versatile. On the ground, or along a branch, they walk on all fours with the tail curled into an S-shape and held over the back. On the ground the fingers are often held bent, so that they may walk partially on their knuckles. They often walk upright with the arms held either down by their sides or else grasping a convenient nearby branch or rail. In the trees the usual mode of locomotion is 'three-handed', using the two hook-like hands and the prehensile tail. Commonly they swing along by their hands like a gibbon, with the tail giving additional support from time to time. They also simply 'drop' 20–30 ft in the trees.

They live high up in the trees, only occasionally descending to the ground, in troops of varying size which are constantly splitting and reforming. Basically the troops consist of groups of females with their young, which may or may not be accompanied by an adult male. The females have a weakly marked rank order among themselves. Males tend to be intolerant of each other in the presence of females, and are always dominant to females. Males groom females; high-ranking ones groom themselves more often than they are groomed.

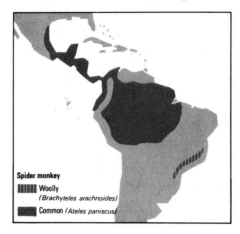

Spider monkey
||||| Woolly
(Brachyteles arachnoides)
■ Common *(Ateles paniscus)*

Feeding with their tails

Spider monkeys use their tails as handy extra limbs on all occasions. When sleeping, they sit huddled, often two or three together, with the tail holding onto a support. Its use seems to be automatic, winding round any object with which it comes into contact. In a zoo a spider monkey will hold a peanut in its tail while transferring it to its mouth.

Spider monkeys eat only fruit. Their diet appears to contain no leaves or insects of any kind. Moreover, they are selective about it, sniffing a fruit to see if it is ripe, even biting into it and rejecting it if it is unsatisfactory. A great deal of food is merely tasted, half-eaten and then dropped.

Kitten play

A pre-mating behaviour known as 'grappling' has been described by Eisenberg and Kuehn. Male and female sit opposite each other on a branch and push and pull, and cuff each other with their fists, slapping and biting one another. The male may then chase the female, often roaring as he does so. Then they fall quiet and return to their sitting positions with the female generally sitting on the male's lap, facing him. This seems to occur mostly in the evening, and since mating has not been observed, it must take place at night. Young have been observed all the year round but there may be 'birth peaks' at times when fruit is especially abundant.

The female's sexual cycle lasts 24–27 days, and gestation is 139 days. The single young clings to the mother's belly at first but after about four months it transfers to her back, with its tail twisted round hers for stability. The young are very playful. They are black for the first six months or so, then assume the adult coloration. Spider monkeys can live up to 20 years.

Victims of expanding commerce

Birds of prey, jaguars and small cats from time to time undoubtedly take adults or, more likely, youngsters. Man also is a predator; the South American Indians have been shooting at spider monkeys for food with their blow-pipes for several thousand years without doing any harm to the populations. What is really threatening these monkeys, as it is threatening all South America's fauna and indeed the Indians themselves, is the callous and selfish attitudes of those who own the forests—the timber and rubber concessions denude the land—and cause the shooting of wildlife and even the slaughtering of Indians.

South American 'apes'

The Omomyidae, the family which gave rise to the higher Primates (monkeys, apes and man), lived in northern Eurasia and North America about 40–60 million years ago. In the Old World were the more familiar monkeys such as the baboons, macaques, colobus, and the apes and man gradually evolved from them. They are known as Catarrhines because of their narrow noses with the nostrils facing forwards. In the Americas the Omomyids somehow got into South America (either there was still a land bridge at that time, or else they got across on 'vegetation rafts' or spread from island to island), and there they evolved into the New World monkeys, which are known as Platyrrhines because of their broad noses with nostrils facing sideways.

In South America there were the same environments as in the Old World, but there were different kinds of monkeys to exploit them, so they came to look very similar to the Old World monkeys and apes, although their common ancestors were the Omomyidae, not monkeys at all! In Africa and Asia, the similar habitats are occupied by guenons, mangabeys, mandrills, colobus and langurs, all leading slightly different ways of life, so avoiding competition, while allowing room for all. This also applies to the apes. In South America, the 'ape' way of life is followed by the spider monkey, and it is interesting to note the characteristics they have in common with apes. Their arm bones are strong with large muscles, and are longer than the legs. The hand is long and narrow, the fingers are long and curved, making the hand into a hook. Apes have a short thumb, but the spider monkey has gone further and has lost it altogether. Thus the spider monkey, through specialising as a fruit-eater like the apes, has become a brachiator too, swinging from the trees, using one arm, then the other, like a gibbon. The fruit they eat generally grows out along the branches which are too thin to walk along, and so the best way to gather it is to hang by the arms underneath the branches.

class	**Mammalia**
order	**Primates**
family	**Cebidae**
genera & species	***Ateles paniscus*** common ***Brachyteles arachnoides*** woolly

▷ *Agile ease of a spider monkey, hanging on with its feet and using its tail for extra support. These monkeys are second only to gibbons in agility, and their ape-like way of life is reflected in many anatomical features.*

Spinetail

Spinetails are a group of swifts with short tails, the feathers of which taper like those of a woodpecker, so the central shaft protrudes beyond the vane. The spiny feathers are used as a prop when the swift is roosting on a vertical surface. The 18 spinetails are found in Africa, Asia and America, and one Asian species migrates to Australia and New Zealand. The best known is the chimney swift which breeds in North America. It is the common swift east of the Mississippi and Missouri rivers and nests as far north as the Gulf of St Lawrence. It winters in Central and South America. The chimney swift is 5 in. long with a dark plumage but whitish on the throat and upper breast. The spines on the tail feathers are not visible in flight and the tail is not fanned. The other North American spinetail is Vaux's swift. Rather smaller than the chimney swift, it is also much paler underneath. It lives to the west of the Rocky Mountains in the northwest United States and south-west Canada. The other spinetails are very similar in appearance to the North American species. The bat-like or Boehm's spinetail of Africa is so named because of its very short tail and broad wings which gives it a bat-like appearance. It is dark above with a greyish-brown throat and upper breast and a white lower breast and abdomen. The largest spinetail, which is also one of the largest of all swifts, is the brown-throated spinetail. It is 7 in. long, dark with a whitish throat streaked with brown and a white abdomen. It ranges from India to the East Indies.

Roosting en masse

As with other swifts, spinetails do not land on the ground voluntarily. Their legs are small and weak and they are unable to spring into the air for take-off. Therefore they roost and nest on vertical surfaces where they can take-off merely by letting go and dropping away. The brown-throated spine-tail is one of the fastest flying swifts and many of the spinetails fly at such great heights when feeding that they cannot be seen with the naked eye. The bat-like spine-tail, however, with its broad wings and short tail is slower but more manoeuvrable than the others. Rather than hunting in great sweeps across the sky, the bat-tailed spine-tail hunts around the tree tops in forests and woods and its manoeuvrability is en-hanced by long secondary flight feathers acting as extra rudders.

Spinetailed swifts roost in colonies, some-times numbering several hundreds, in chimneys, hollow trees and in the open. An example of an open roost was found early one morning in California when the chimney swifts were migrating southwards. They were roosting on a tree trunk and were packed in a solid mass 4 ft long, 18 in. wide and 3 swifts deep. The swifts were inert and could be picked off the tree and handled, but 2 hours after sunrise they became active and flew off. Regular roosts in chimneys and trees are used year after year. Each evening the swifts fly above the roost in a dense mass then stream down into the roost like a cloud of smoke disappear-ing backwards into a chimney.

Flying diet

Spinetail swifts eat insects caught in flight. These are mainly flies, bugs, mayflies and stoneflies. Some nestling chimney swifts were once found to have been fed on fleas but it is not known where these came from.

Time-saving nests

Courtship takes place on the wing, then the pair prospect for a nest site and mate there. With the exception of the large brown-throated spinetail which nests at the bottoms of tree hollows, spinetails build their nests on vertical surfaces in hollow trees, large chimneys, and in the case of the bat-like spinetail, occasionally in mine shafts. The nest is made of twigs which are broken off with the feet and carried in the bill, and then cemented with saliva to form a bowl-shaped nest. Fresh saliva has the consistency of glycerine and in a few hours sets to form a tough solid.

Egg-laying, in the chimney swift at least, starts when the nest is only half built. This appears to be a time-saving device, the nest being completed before the chicks start to put on weight. The clutch of the chimney swift is 4—5 eggs, 7 in Vaux's swift, and they are incubated by both parents for 19 days. The chicks are brooded at night for another 12 days. They leave the nest at 14—19 days but do not take their first flight outside until 30 days old. They spend the intervening time clinging with strong claws to the wall of the hollow or chimney.

New nesting places

Before Europeans settled in North America the chimney swift nested and roosted in hollow trees but as civilisation spread it started to use large chimneys and now it is very unusual to find a chimney swift nest in a tree. The new habit has allowed the chimney swift to extend its range into new regions where there are no trees. At times it is rather a problem, for lighting a fire may kill hundreds of swifts roosting in the flue and if for some reason they decide to fly down, a room can be completely ruined as walls, carpets and furniture become covered with soot and droppings. Altogether five spinetails have formed the habit of nesting in man-made structures. Vaux's spinetail, which still nests mainly in trees, took to nesting in chimneys in this century. A South American species was first found nesting in a chimney in 1948.

class	**Aves**
order	**Apodiformes**
family	**Apodidae**
genus & species	***Chaetura pelagica*** *chimney swift* ***C. gigantea*** *brown-throated spinetail* ***C. boehmi*** *bat-like spinetail* ***C. vauxi*** *Vaux's spinetail, others*

▷ *Upside down and the right way up. Two chimney swifts, one resting on its chest, the other supported by its spiny tail, perch on a tree trunk. They are birds of the air and seldom land on the ground, their legs being very weak.*

Lynwood Chase

F Collet

Spiny anteater

This strange looking animal, like the platypus, is an egg-laying mammal living in Australasia. It is also known as echidna, native porcupine and even spiny porcupine. It looks rather like a hedgehog but is larger, and like the hedgehog, but more so, it is very strong. In the Australian echidna the head and body are up to 18 in. long, and the tail is short, stubby and naked and only about 3 in. long. It may be over 10 lb in weight and there is a record of one weighing just over 14 lb. The back of its squat body is covered with long sharp spines over 2 in. long. These are usually yellow at the base and black at the tip, but are sometimes entirely yellow. They are interspersed with coarse brown hair which is usually almost hidden by the spines. The underparts are covered with hair only. There is no neck and the small external ears are not usually visible. The small eyes are at the base of the long, tapering snout which has a small toothless mouth. The long sticky tongue can be shot out as much as 6 or 7 in. The legs are short and stout and each of the enormously strong forefeet has five long curved claws which are used for digging. The second of the five toes on the hindfoot is long and is used for grooming. All males, and some females, have short ankle spurs.

There are two genera. Tachyglossus has one species in Australia and New Guinea, which is divided into four subspecies which differ in only small details, and another species in Tasmania which is larger, has a shorter snout and has short spines largely hidden by the hair. There are three species of the long-nosed spiny anteater Zaglossus, found only in New Guinea. It is up to 39 in. long and weighs up to 21 lb. Its very long snout curves downwards and it has an extremely long tongue. The legs are much longer than in the Tachyglossus species.

Powerful digger

Spiny anteaters live in a wide variety of habitats ranging from hot dry deserts and humid rainforests to rocky ridges and valleys, up to an altitude of 5–6 000 ft in the Australian Alps where the air temperature in the three coldest months is rarely above freezing. The New Guinea species of *Zaglossus* inhabit humid forests at altitudes ranging from 3 770–9 400 ft.

The echidna is generally solitary. It can run swiftly and climb well. It walks with the legs fully extended so that the stomach is relatively high off the ground, and with the hind toes directed outward and backward, giving it a somewhat grotesque appearance. It shelters in burrows or crevices among rocks and when disturbed digs into the earth at great speed, descending vertically so that the spines are uppermost. If the earth is too hard for digging it will roll up, presenting an armature of spines to a potential aggressor.

It used to be thought that the echidna was nocturnal but it seems that it comes out to feed especially in the afternoon and is, furthermore, about during all hours of daylight. It spends much of its time, however, rolled up, presumably asleep, when it is not actively foraging.

Licking up its food

Spiny anteaters feed mainly on termites which they lick up into their mouths with their long sticky tongues. The jaws are toothless; the insects are scraped off the tongue by spines on the roof of the mouth, and crushed between these and spines on the base of the tongue as it is thrust out again. There seems to be a difference of opinion about what they eat. Vincent Serventy has stated that he has never seen a spiny anteater take food other than termites. Other investigators say they eat ants, but only when the ants are crawling among termites. Like hedgehogs, tame echidnas will drink large quantities of milk. They will also take bread, milk, and minced meat. The New Guinea echidna in captivity has been found to eat earthworms, grasping them either by the head or the tail and sucking them into the mouth.

Spiny anteaters are said to be able to go for as much as a month without food.

Egg-laying mammal

One egg is laid a year, occasionally two, and this finds its way into a pouch which appears on the female's belly at the beginning of the breeding season, which lasts from early July to late September. The pouch later disappears. No one knows how the egg reaches the pouch. Presumably the mother pushes it in with her snout. The egg is small and spherical, with a soft parchment-like covering. It hatches in about 10–11 days. The baby breaks out by using its egg tooth and is suckled inside the pouch with milk secreted from slits in the mother's abdomen. The young echidna remains in the pouch until its spines are sufficiently developed that the mother must eject it. She then places it in a burrow and visits it every 1½–2 days to feed it until it is weaned about 3 months later when it weighs about 2 lb. Echidnas become sexually mature at the end of one year, and live up to 50 years.

Few enemies

They have few natural enemies. The aborigines eat them and the flesh is said to have a characteristic smell of crushed ants. Fortunately it is never a pest nor has any economic values for man to exploit, so it cannot be in much danger.

Hibernation?

A curious feature of the spiny anteater is its alleged hibernation, frequently mentioned by those who write about the animal. The mere idea is odd because New Guinea, which forms part of the range of the spiny anteater, is almost on the Equator, the mainland of Australia is partly tropical and partly subtropical and even Tasmania, the most southerly part of its range, barely comes within latitudes that, in the northern hemisphere, are associated with hibernation.

The spiny anteater has a normal body temperature that is lower than most mammals, its upper limit being 32.5°C/90°F. So long as it has sufficient food it can endure temperatures down to 5°C/41°F. Should it fail to find sufficient food when the air temperature has dropped to this level, it then becomes dormant. This is more like the behaviour of reptiles. Another reptilian feature is that heat stroke may occur at high temperatures. The spiny anteater is in distress at temperatures above 35°C/95°F and dies of heat stroke at 38°C/100°F. Nevertheless it can live in deserts where the shade temperature may go up to 49°C/120 F by going underground and sheltering in the cool of a cave.

class	**Mammalia**
order	**Monotremata**
family	**Tachyglossidae**
genera & species	***Tachyglossus aculeatus*** *Australian or short-nosed spiny anteater* ***T. setosus*** *Tasmanian spiny anteater* ***Zaglossus bruijni*** *New Guinea or long-nosed spiny anteater* *others*

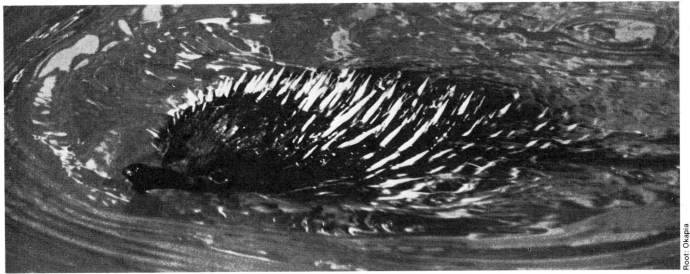

◁ *Spiny earth-shifter: when disturbed, the Australian spiny anteater can disappear into the ground in a flurry of earth and a very short time. Once body-down in the ground it is safe; the sharp spines are an efficient deterrent. If caught on hard ground, it will roll, hedgehog fashion, into a ball.*

△ *Paddling echidna: unlike the closely related platypus, it is not a strong swimmer, and takes to water only when pursued.*

▷ *Smacking its lips with a long, sticky tongue, an Australian echidna — paradoxically called also the short-nosed echidna — poises, massive feet at the ready, as if in anticipation of a termite meal. The comic looks are, however, deceptive; the spiny anteaters are powerful animals, capable of tearing open termite nests and trees, and of digging at phenomenal speed.*

▽ *A long-nosed spiny anteater probes around a rotten log for insects. It lives in rocky country in New Guinea. Like the Australian echidna it is a digger, but has less efficient tools, having only short foreclaws.*

Jane Burton: Photo Res

Barry Pengilley

△ *Two elephant trunk fish **Macrognathus** **aculeatus**. Normally they hide in the mud during the day with only the tips of their long snouts protruding; when they leave it the eye spots on the tail distract attention from the head region.*

Spiny eel

Spiny eels have nothing to do with true eels except that some of them are eel-shaped. Others are more band-shaped, flattened from side to side with the body only six times as long as it is deep. They are named for the row of spines along the back. These number 7—40, according to the species. The spines lie in front of the soft-rayed dorsal fin and can be raised or lowered. Some spiny eels, when handled, try to wriggle backwards with the spines erect, which can be very painful.

Most of the 50 species are less than 15 in. long, the longest being 3 ft. In colour they are mainly some shade of brown on the back and yellow to pale brown on the belly. This dull background is enlivened by attractive patterns of spots, irregular stripes or reticulate patterns along the flanks. The head of the spiny eel tapers sharply to the snout which curves slightly down. The double nostrils, found in so many fishes, are widely separated. The rear opening on each side lies just in front of the eye. The front opening is tubular and hangs down near the tip of the snout. The mouth and gill openings are small. The dorsal and anal fins start about the middle of the body and are usually continuous round the tail tip. The pectoral fins are small, the pelvic fins absent.

Spiny eels live in the fresh and brackish waters of tropical and southern Africa, and they extend north to southern Asia, southern China and eastwards to the Malay Archipelago.

Mud dwellers

Spiny eels live mainly in waters with a muddy or sandy bottom with plenty of aquatic plants. They swim with side to side serpentine movements of the body, helped by the wave-like action of the fins. During the day they lie hidden among water plants or buried in the mud or sand. Some species dig themselves in until only the eyes and nostrils are exposed at the surface. To do this they rock the body from side to side, at the same time thrusting forward with the snout. Many breathe air, rising to the surface to gulp it, and these fish can survive indefinitely in foul waters deficient in oxygen.

Hog-nosed feeding

In the evening the spiny eels leave their daytime hideouts to feed. The long mobile snout, which is strengthened with a rod of cartilage, is very sensitive. With it, and helped by the tubular nostrils, the spiny eel feels around for prey then sucks it in with a jerky movement. It will also forage in the mud, rooting into it more like a hog. The food of spiny eels is mainly worms, insect larvae and small crustaceans.

Hide-and-seek babies

At the onset of the breeding season they pair, the males chasing the females, which are more robust than the males, and nudging them in the region of the vent with their snouts. The eggs appear to be scattered over the bottom, but what happens after this is not known. The eels are difficult to observe in the wild and although they have several times bred in captivity, it is not known for most species exactly how long the eggs take to hatch since the baby fishes immediately hide themselves along the thickest tangles of plants or bury themselves in the soft surface of the mud. Derek McInerny, in the 1969 edition of his book *All About Tropical Fish*, has described the breeding of one species. The eggs hatched in 3 days and the baby fishes, which were completely ignored by the parents, lacked the long snout. This did not begin to show until they were a month old.

△ *A family feature:* **Macrognathus armatus**, *like all mastacembelids, have flat elongated heads. The very sensitive snout is supported by special cartilage. The two anterior nostrils and the snout form a trilobed appendage.*

Several defences

Since so little is known about these fishes it is not surprising there should be no information about their enemies. These must be few, however, for spiny eels have the colour of the mud in which they hide and, moreover, they have a disruptive pattern on their bodies, which tends to break up their outline, making them inconspicuous if they swim about in broad daylight among water plants. From the experience of the few who have tried to collect them it seems that the eels dive into the mud as soon as they are disturbed. Nevertheless, they are caught and eaten in some places, no doubt the local people having their own special methods for catching them. In other places, however, they are avoided because they look like snakes. They are harmless, however, having no venom and only tiny teeth in their very small mouths.

Mystery snout

There is one species of spiny eel *Macrognathus aculeatus* which looks more like a caricature than a real fish. It has been called the elephant trunk fish. It has a long, very mobile snout which is slightly prehensile. On the underside of the snout are 20—26 pairs of toothed plates carried on a forward extension of the upper jaw. How it uses this is not known for certain, but from the look of it one might suppose that it uses it in the same way as an elephant uses its trunk—to put food into its mouth.

class	**Pisces**
order	**Perciformes**
family	**Mastacembelidae**
genus & species	*Mastacembelus armatus* *others*

Spiny mouse

The spiny mouse of Africa and Asia is yet another example of a mammal with a spiny coat whose sharp prickles have been evolved from soft hairs, presumably for self-protection. There are five species ranging from 2¾ in. to nearly 5 in. in head and body length, with a tail about the same length. The average weight of an adult of the larger species is 2–3 oz. The colour on the upperparts varies from pale yellowish, reddish brown and reddish to dark grey while the underparts are white. The back and the tail are covered with coarse, rigid grooved spines. The tail, which is scaly and nearly naked, is very brittle and is easily lost. It may be whitish above and below, bicoloured or uniformly dark. The snout is pointed, the ears are large and erect, and like most mice, the eyes are large and bright.

The typical species is the Cairo spiny

Competing with gerbils

Spiny mice usually live in rocky country but in parts of their range are found in woodland undergrowth and in desert areas. In the desert they will often use gerbil burrows for shelter and when food is scarce may compete with the gerbils for food. They usually come out to feed in the early morning and late afternoon but individuals have been seen about at all hours.

Eating anything

In the wild spiny mice eat mainly seeds and other plant foods. Some of them live in or near human habitations, however, and these, like the house mice, will feed on nearly anything they can find. They have even been known to chew such things as fibre mats. In desert areas they have been observed feeding on snails.

Active young

The young of most spiny mice are born between February and September. The Cairo spiny mouse shows unusual breeding behaviour. It has a long gestation period for

standing up, the young ones generally being delivered backwards. This is most unusual in rodents and is more like what happens with the large hoofed animals. The Cairo spiny mouse is unique among the Muridae in having her 2–3 young born fully furred and with their eyes open, showing none of the helplessness of most newly-born rodents. A curious habit has been observed in the young of licking their mother's saliva but the reason is unknown.

Unlike the Cairo spiny mouse the young of *Acomys dimidiatus*, a related species, are born blind and the eyes open on the third day. Weaning occurs about 2 weeks after birth when they weigh about ½ oz.

Male spiny mice are sexually mature at about 7 weeks old. The growth of the male is almost complete at the end of about 150 days although the weight tends to increase slightly up to the third year. A curious phenomenon, for which there is no ready explanation is that shortly before the death of a spiny mouse the animal becomes slightly emaciated and there are wide fluctuations in its weight.

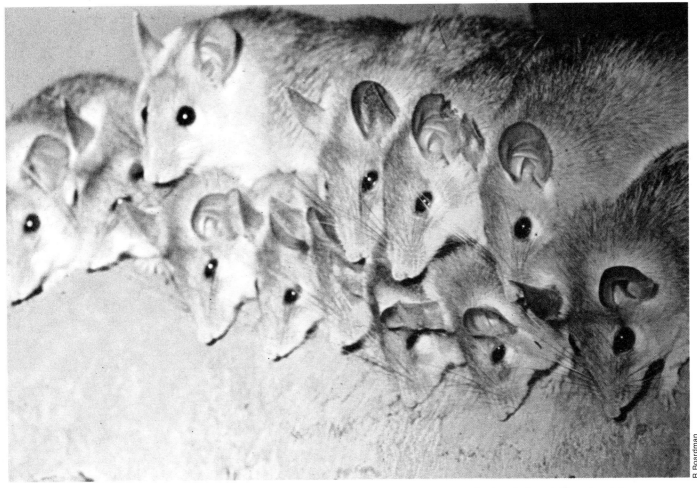

R Boardman

mouse, named from specimens found in the Cairo area at the beginning of the 19th century. The remaining species range from India through southwest Asia to much of Africa. These include the golden spiny mouse from northeast Africa and southwest Asia which is distinguished by the black soles to its feet and the Cape spiny mouse of South Africa which is less prickly than the typical species.

the size of the animal, about 38 days, and just before the birth of her young the female shows an exaggerated maternal urge and will often steal a neighbour's baby, holding it in her paws to groom it and she may even suckle it. In the absence of any young ones around she may even try to groom an adult, trying to hold it in her paws as though it were a baby. The female does not retire from her fellows when about to give birth and actually gives birth

△ *A gathering of spiny mice at the zoo. Although the native habitat of **Acomys cahirinus** is rocky and sandy areas of the Near East, it also lives in areas of dense vegetation, where it seems to prefer the crevices of termite hills. In Egypt it is mainly found near human habitation. It is easy to keep in captivity, and breeds rapidly. Spiny mice often huddle together, presumably liking the body contact. Unfortunately the tail is very brittle and in crowded conditions it easily breaks off.*

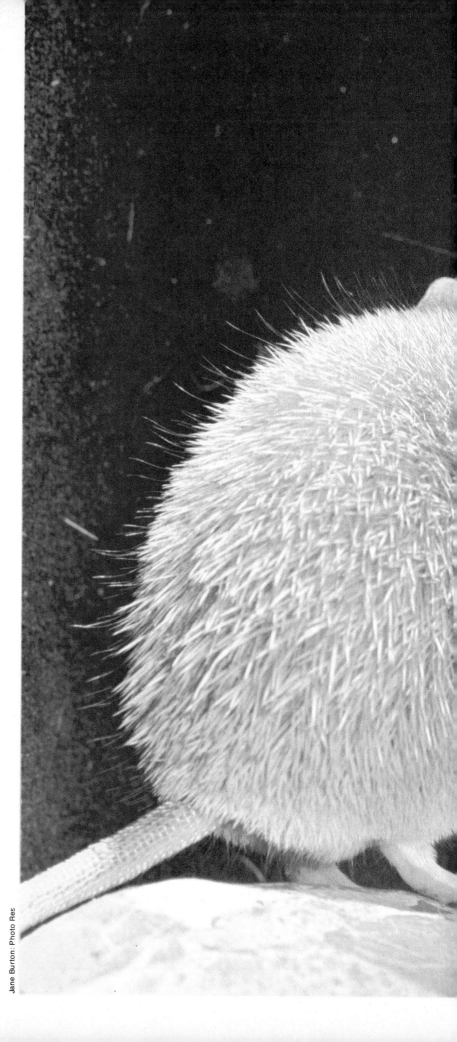

▷ *A Cairo spiny mouse carefully watches over her two-week-old baby as it washes its tail. Before the young are born the female develops a powerful maternal urge—she will even try to steal a neighbour's baby.*

Silk purse to sow's ear

The African and Asian spiny mice are the best known, but there are other species in the New World. In tropical America, from Guyana and Brazil to Panama, there are four species of so called spiny mice but these belong to the family Cricetidae, the vole family. Another, in Ecuador, is known from six specimens only, collected in 1924, and not seen since. In Central America, northwards through Mexico to Texas, are 21 species of spiny pocket mice of the family Heteromyidae. Apart from their stiff coats they differ little from ordinary voles and pocket mice, and their coats are not all equally spiny, some being covered in little more than stout bristles. Perhaps their main importance lies entirely in the study of their hair in relation to other spiny mammals. For example, it may seem an exaggeration to say that the spines of a hedgehog are no more than modified hairs. It might be difficult to believe that such spines could possibly be evolved from the soft silky hairs of some of the better known mice. Yet if we could take samples of spines from all these spiny rodents, we could sort them out in ascending thickness and spininess to give an almost complete gradation from fine silky hair to a hedgehog's spines.

class	**Mammalia**
order	**Rodentia**
family	**Muridae**
genus & species	*Acomys cahirinus* Cairo spiny mouse **A. subspinosus** Cape spiny mouse others

Spoonbill

The spoonbills, related to the ibises, are remarkable for the peculiar shape of the bill. The six species of spoonbills are up to 2½ ft long from the tip of the bill to the end of the tail and they have long legs. The bill is long, flattened horizontally and broadened to a spatulate or flattened spoon shape at the end. All have almost wholly white plumage except for the roseate spoonbill of America, in which the adult plumage is tinged with pink, deepening to red on the shoulders. The legs are pink and the bill is yellow. The roseate spoonbill ranges from the southern United States through much of South America. The common or European spoonbill has a black bill tipped with yellow, black legs, an orange patch on the throat and a yellowish patch at the base of the neck in summer, when it also has a drooping crest at the back of the head. It breeds in parts of northern and southern Europe, southern Asia and Africa. The lesser spoonbill of China and Japan is very like it, and so are the royal or black-billed spoonbills and the yellow-billed or yellow-legged spoonbills of Australia. Some ornithologists are inclined to the view that these four Old World spoonbills are just geographical races of one species. The African spoonbill differs from the rest in having bare red skin on the face, some red on the bill and bright pink legs. It lives throughout Africa south of the Sahara and in Madagascar.

◁ *Make way! A European spoonbill joins his fellow spoonbills and long-tailed cormorants.*
△ *Brakes on, a roseate spoonbill lands.* ▽ *Legs trailing, European spoonbills take off.*

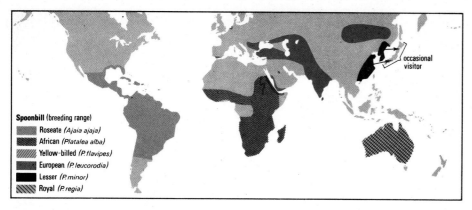

Spoonbill (breeding range)
- Roseate *(Ajaia ajaja)*
- African *(Platalea alba)*
- Yellow-billed *(P. flavipes)*
- European *(P. leucorodia)*
- Lesser *(P. minor)*
- Royal *(P. regia)*

occasional visitor

Damage from drainage

The main enemies of spoonbills are their own bills and the way they feed. Both are specialized to give the maximum return from feeding in the shallow waters of marshes and in shallow lagoons and lakes. These are the first to go when land is drained to reclaim it for agriculture. For example, spoonbills used to breed in parts of England up to the 17th century. Then the draining of marshes robbed them of the habitat necessary for their peculiar bills and ways of feeding. That is not the whole story so far as Britain is concerned for even in the last 20 years when they have had legal protection, they have been shot for their skins for private collections, and even for fear they might damage pheasant reserves! However, the greatest threat to their existence is land drainage and it is the peculiar habitat requirements of spoonbills that account for their scattered distribution. In Europe, for example, they are most plentiful in Holland and the Danube basin.

class	**Aves**
order	**Ciconiiformes**
family	**Threskiornithidae**
genera & species	***Ajaia ajaja*** *roseate spoonbill* ***Platalea alba*** *African spoonbill* ***P. flavipes*** *yellow-billed spoonbill* ***P. leucorodia*** *European spoonbill* ***P. minor*** *lesser spoonbill* ***P. regia*** *royal spoonbill*

▽ *Follow the leader. A line of African spoonbills, easily distinguishable from other species by their bright pink legs, feed in the failing light of dusk. While wading in the shallows, spoonbills feed on small fish, aquatic insects and crustaceans, which they catch by holding their bills almost vertical, partly open and moving them rapidly from side to side. The bills, horizontally flattened and broadened at the end into a thin spatula, are specially adapted to feeding in shallow water.*

Sweeping for food

All spoonbills are alike in their habits except that the New World species has less tendency to nest on the ground. They live together in loose flocks, often in the company of ibises, herons and egrets, all relatives of the spoonbills. They are found mainly near shallow fresh water or in marshes. They swim only occasionally, but perch in trees, often high up. Their flight is slow with regular wingbeats, and they sometimes glide and soar. A party of spoonbills fly in a single file at fairly regular intervals, with their necks stretched forward.

During the day spoonbills rest and sleep by the edge of the water, sometimes on one leg. They may feed a little by day but they usually feed at dusk. The spoonbill holds its bill vertically downwards and sweeps the spatulate end from side to side underwater, keeping the bill slightly open to grasp anything edible. At times the bird rushes here and there, backwards and forwards as if frantic, probably chasing an elusive quarry. Although a small amount of seeds and fibrous plant matter have usually been found in the stomachs of dead spoonbills their food is mainly animal. It includes the usual insect larvae and aquatic insects as well as leeches, worms, water snails, frog spawn, tadpoles and the small fishes that haunt the shallows.

Silent nesting

Spoonbills are very silent birds. They are said to give a low grunt when disturbed at their nesting places and the nestlings are said to squeak and wheeze. When excited, as at breeding time, they use their bills as clappers, at the same time raising the feathers on their crest. Courtship seems also to be accompanied by the kind of dancing seen in storks, but this has only rarely been observed. Usually they nest in reed beds or in low bushes, on islands in the marshy lagoons, but the site varies much and in Asia the nests are more often in tall trees. The birds nest in colonies of a few to 200 pairs, the nests being built often only a few feet apart. Both of the pair build the nest, which is made of reeds or sticks piled to a height of 1½ ft. Usually 4 eggs are laid. They are a dull white with sparse brown markings. The eggs are incubated for 3 weeks by both parents who also feed the downy young which remain in the nest for 4−5 weeks and return to it regularly for another 2−3 weeks by which time they are able to fly. At first the nestling has a normal bill but the spoon-shape is soon grown. They are fed by the parents regurgitating food into their throats, then opening their bills wide and allowing the chicks to thrust their massive bills in to take the partly digested food.

Springbok

The springbok is a South African gazelle, a beautiful and lively antelope famous for its pronking. It is larger than most gazelles, standing 30–35 in. high and weighing 65–70 lb. Typically reddish fawn, it is white underneath with a black stripe along the flanks separating the fawn from the white. The springbok has a mainly whitish face with only a narrow black stripe through the eye to the nose partly obliterating the typical gazelline face-markings. The horns are ringed and slightly divergent with strongly incurved tips, and they are smaller in females. From the middle of the back to the rump, is a large pocket-like gland. When the animal is excited this turns inside out revealing a broad display of erect, pure white hairs, which acts as a warning signal to others. The first animal alerted shows these hairs and the signal is taken up and passed through the ranks.

Springbok live in the Kalahari desert of southwest Africa, extending into Botswana. They extend also into the western side of Cape Province and the Orange Free State, but are no longer as numerous as they used to be in these areas.

Retreat en masse

The name springbok comes from their habit of 'pronking'. This is by no means confined to this species—indeed, it is found in all gazelles—but the pronk of the springbok is a most remarkable sight. The animal leaps 10–12 ft into the air with the body curved and the legs stiff and close together, pointing downwards. The head is held low. The whole effect is very like bouncing. Generally the dorsal gland is everted during pronking and this acts as an additional warning signal in times of danger. When the enemy, whether leopard, lion, cheetah, or wild dog, has been located and all nearby animals alerted to it, the whole herd begins to run. With their bodies fully extended, they run low over the ground, like blesbok.

Springbok live in large herds, the social structure of which is not well known. The herd is probably made up of territorial males, each with its mixture of females and young males, as in many gazelles. Their dry habitat means that they must range over wide areas to find sufficient food, which is mainly grass.

Migration a thing of the past

When they were abundant throughout the western region of southern Africa, springbok would migrate, in times of drought, across South Africa from the Kalahari, over the Orange River, to the Cape. The migrations were carried out by a massed and continuous seething tide of springbok. Other antelope which could not get out of the way would be engulfed and swept along too, whether they wanted to or not. Between short snatched feeding bouts, the springbok would press on regardless, those in front always being pushed onward by those behind, so large-scale mishaps were com-

Pronking for pleasure: a springbok demonstrates its remarkable pronk, which it does in play or when alarmed. On touching the ground again it quickly rebounds, giving the appearance of bouncing.

mon. Hundreds would be drowned in the Orange River as they crossed it, and when they came to the coast even in the sea! Since droughts occurred irregularly so did the migrations. Modern studies of animals that undertake vast periodic migrations, like the lemmings, tend to suggest that a cyclically exploding population is itself the cause of the food shortage. In lemmings the large litter sizes lead to exploding populations. In the springbok the strictly seasonal breeding would produce a sudden, huge population increase, and in the kind of poor environment in which they lived there would be no alternative but to move on to 'greener pastures'.

The last recorded springbok migration was in 1896. After that, the populations never built up again. They were shot for food and for sport, and their range was fenced off and divided up, producing the largely isolated, inbred populations that we see today. There are still, however, a large number—perhaps millions—living under wild conditions in the Kalahari, especially around Etosha Pan, the great natural oasis that has been made into a reserve.

Typical gazelle courtship

Since they belong to the gazelle group of antelope, springbok have an elaborate courtship pattern, including the *Laufschlag* or 'leg-beat' (see p 1635) when the male places his stiff foreleg between the female's hind-legs and makes stroking motions against her legs. This is the characteristic motion which stimulates the female to mate. The gestation lasts 170 days. The young are born in November and December, and are dependent on their mothers for about six months.

Strange colours

In the north of their range, in southern Angola and northern southwest Africa, lives a larger race, the Angolan springbok. This has a longer, narrower head with horns in line with the face. The female's horns are bigger in this race, as are the ears, and the whole colour of the coat is brighter. This is a distinct geographical population. Further south, the common springbok has several abnormal colour phases. The differences between these are much more striking than the differences separating the Angolan and common races, but they do not correspond to geographic populations, so are not classified as distinct races.

Some of these colour oddities are remarkable. On the farm of Mr JH van der Merwe at Droëfontein in the Noupoort district are many partly discoloured springbok: some are quite white, others have a brown flank or a brown facial stripe. Such forms have never been recorded in the wild, and they are probably the result of inbreeding on the Karroo farms, which 'fix' mutations that would disappear completely almost as soon as they arose in the wild. Near Murraysburg, 37 'black' springbok have been reported living in a herd of 300. They are, in fact, 'gun-metal brown', with a white face-blaze, and they look strikingly like blesbok. These also are the result of inbreeding in an enclosed population.

class	**Mammalia**
order	**Artiodactyla**
family	**Bovidae**
genus & species	*Antidorcas marsupialis marsupialis* common springbok *A. m. angolensis* Angolan springbok

▽ *A group of common springboks with a large gemsbok standing several yards away. When springboks were abundant, large migrating herds of up to 8 000 could be seen, sweeping other antelopes, willing or not, along with them.*

Springhare

Although Peter Pallas, the celebrated 18th-century naturalist called it a mouse, this kangaroo-like African animal has since been called, more appropriately, a jumping hare, or springhaas in Afrikaans. It is 17 in. long in head and body with the tail slightly longer, and it weighs up to 9 lb. It has a relatively large rounded head, with a blunt muzzle, prominent eyes, long, pointed, widely separated ears, which have a tendency to droop to the sides, long hind legs and very short front legs. Its long, soft coat is sandy to reddish with some long black hairs. The underparts are white and the bushy tail is black in the outer half. Each forefoot has five toes with long, sharp claws and the four toes on each hindfoot have nail-like claws. The second toe from the outside on the hindfoot is longer than the rest.

*There is a single species ranging over most of Africa south of the Sahara. A form in Kenya has been considered a separate species but is now generally accepted as only a subspecies. Zoologists seem to be agreed that the springhare is a rodent but there the agreement ends. It has, at various times, been placed with the squirrels, the porcupines, the jerboas, the scalytails, and now, purely as a matter of convenience, if not in a mood of despair, it is placed quite non-committally in a family of its own between the scalytails and the dormice, with the name **Pedetes capensis**.*

Digs like a rabbit

The remaining information on this unusual animal is meagre despite the nearly 200 years since it was first made known to scientists. Perhaps this is because it is so largely nocturnal. It is never out before dark and is back underground again before dawn. The front paws are used in digging, the sharp claws being effective picks and rakes. The ears have a small tragus or earlet, said to keep sand out of its ears when it is digging, but this is no more than an inspired guess. It is said to close the entrances to its burrows with plugs of earth and if this is so, the feat suggests considerable engineering skill, since the openings to the burrows are large. The burrows themselves are known as warrens, and a single warren may spread over an area 100 yd across. Each warren has four or five openings, and it may be inhabited by a colony, although within the warren it would appear that each individual occupies a separate sleeping chamber. Its food is roots and bulbs, grain and other such vegetable matter, and it is said to scratch up sprouting grains to take the germinating seeds below. The jumping hare is no friend of the farmer.

◁ *Except for its long bushy tail, the springhare has a kangaroo-like appearance. Although it is nocturnal in the wild, it adapts well to captivity, becoming active during the day. It makes an interesting pet and will learn to follow its owner around.*

▽ *On the run—the springhare is not as fast as was once supposed. Although able to leap 5 ft at one bound, it avoids predators by dodging, swerving and jinking.*

Firsthand encounter

There seems to be general agreement that the jumping hare is a great wanderer. It moves mainly by leaping, using only the hindlegs. It becomes quadrupedal when feeding, but when resting it sits upright on its haunches. It is said to go as much as 6—12 miles in a night in search of food, and there are reports that it may wander up to 20 miles for water during a period of drought. Progression is said to be by leaps of 6—9 ft, and it is said to use any road or pathway for easier travelling. This may well be so, since it does not leap very high above the ground and appears to have difficulty in travelling through the savannah grass. Because the trajectory of its leaps is low it is very surprising that the springhare should be credited with leaps of up to 20 or 30 ft and Bourlière states that it sometimes covers 36 ft in one bound. Mr Kim Taylor tested a jumping hare by pursuing one for five minutes. The chase consisted of his running after the hare, which lolloped along, with leaps of no more than 5 ft, until he had almost caught up with it. Then the hare would set off again at a slightly smarter pace, outdistancing him for a while then slowing down until its human pursuer was again almost on top of it before starting off on another spurt. One advantage the jumping hare has over its human pursuer is its skill at jinking, and this, as with the true hares, clearly lies in the long hindlegs but it has an added advantage over the true hare; it progresses bipedally, and so can swerve rapidly at a sharp angle from its previous path. The rapidity of the jinking is, in fact, one of the more noticeable features of its evasive tactics, according to Mr Taylor who knows from experience.

Exaggerated claims for leaps?

This adventure gives some basis for estimating the probable speed of a jumping hare. A human runner, at the top of his form, can reach anything up to 25 mph in a short sprint. An athletic young man would probably be reaching between 15 and 20 mph in the short bursts such as have been described in this chase. Possibly, therefore, the hare was touching about 25 mph in its spurts, but it seems fairly clear that its average rate must be much less than this, and that it is not accustomed to maintaining even that speed for very long.

One striking feature of this chase was that at no time, even when hotly pressed, did the springhare make a leap of more than 5 ft, so if we are to judge the powers of its leaps by this one occasion and this one individual, the records of 20 or 30 ft and especially that of 36 ft seem astonishing.

Slow rate of multiplication

There are varying estimates of the rate of reproduction. Lydekker states there are 3 or 4 young in a litter; other reports give a single young at a birth, rarely twins. There is probably only one litter a year, born in an unlined burrow. At birth a baby weighs just under 9 oz. Its eyes open at two days. A springhare has lived 7½ years in captivity. Although this is a slow rate of reproduction springhares show little sign of reduction in numbers. They are still numerous and widespread although the density of their populations thins out towards the northern parts of their range.

Catch your hare!

Evidently the jumping hare is a favourite among Africans for the pot and there are several ways, we are told, in which it is caught. One is for the hunters to pour in water, flooding the warren, and then to catch the springhare as it bolts from cover. This must be one of the more strenuous ways, for a lot of water is needed. The second is to fasten several reeds end to end, making a flexible rod 15—20 ft long, with a stout wire hook at the end, and to fish the animal out of its burrow. A third method is to run it down, and this, as we have seen, is feasible, if strenuous. The fourth, most favoured method, is to 'shine' it at night. Tradition has it that the jumping hare is drawn to camp fires by curiosity. Whether it is that, or whether light shining in its eyes bewilders it, must be a matter of opinion. Its large eyes, typical of nocturnal animals, glow red when a torch is shone on them from the side, and green when the light is directed at them from the front. Whatever the significance of this, the fact remains that a light shone on a springhare at night puts it at a disadvantage and tends to immobilise it.

Des Bartlett: Photo Res

class	**Mammalia**
order	**Rodentia**
family	**Pedetidae**
genus & species	***Pedetes capensis***

Springtail

The springtails, the most numerous and widespread primitive insects, are equipped with a unique jumping mechanism. They are sufficiently unlike the majority of insects to make it doubtful whether they should be included in the class Insecta. The segments of the thorax, for example, are partly fused together and the abdomen is short and made up of only five or six segments. Moreover, they have no wings and there is no sign that they or their ancestors, found as fossils in Devonian rocks 400 million years old, ever had them. On the other hand they have three pairs of legs, and also agree with the more typical insects in their antennae and other features, including their simple eyes or ocelli, although these are absent in some species of springtails.

and dark coloured, and are covered with hairs and scales and have long antennae. Among these springtails are the ones most frequently seen. Those that live deeper in the humus are white, have short antennae and a sparse body covering and are smaller and sluggish (sometimes lacking the jumping apparatus).

At home everywhere

Springtails live in a wide variety of damp habitats including soil, dead vegetation, particularly the mats that accumulate at the bases of plants, leaf litter, under fallen logs or stones and under bark. One of the few positively useful insects is *Hypogastrura viatica* for it lives in the filter-beds of sewage works feeding on algae and fungi that would choke the beds up if left unchecked. New beds are always 'inoculated' with a few spadesful of material from an old one to make sure that a new population of the springtails becomes established. *Hypogastrura armata* is a pest in

Breathing through the skin

The cuticle of springtails is not waterproof as in other insects so they breathe by taking oxygen out of water passing through the cuticle. *Podura aquatica* that lives on water, immerses from time to time but mostly stays above the water because although its claws are hydrophilic, the rest of its legs are hydrophobic. The surface of clean glass is easily wetted—it is hydrophilic; waxed surface throws off water—it is hydrophobic. So the springtail rests on the surface with only its claws in the surface film, being held steady by the hydrophilic tube.

Another peculiarity is that some springtails give out light. There is no obvious reason for this, so the light must be merely a byproduct of its physiology. Many springtails have eyes; they are simple ocelli 6–8 on each side of the head, each made up of a ring of retinal cells with a lens above them and a cornea beyond. The ocelli are like those on the heads of caterpillars, and the compound eyes of higher insects are made up of ommatidia, thousands of elements very like ocelli all packed together.

Tiny scavengers

Springtails feed on decaying plant and animal matter, or on living plants, as with the lucerne fly. Many of the litter-dwelling species reduce leaves to skeletons or feed on fungi. They probably also eat microscopic plants such as diatoms and single-celled algae. Some species have mouthparts modified for biting, others for sucking.

Pincushion courting

Reproduction is simple, almost casual. The males deposit their sperms in spermatophores which are tiny rounded droplets, each on a fine stalk like microscopic pins on the surfaces of plants. Later a female comes across a spermatophore and places her sexual opening over it, causing the sperm to be released. Growth of the young is direct; there is no metamorphosis. The hatchlings are like miniature adults.

The first gliders?

The spring of a springtail is unique only in structure and the way it is used. Springtails are, however, only one of many kinds of insects that jump. Fleas come readily to mind and click beetles (p 453) have their own novel method. Cheese maggots also jump. They are larvae of a beetle *Piophila*. A cheese maggot grapples the tip of its abdomen with hooks on its mouth, then suddenly lets go. There are also flea beetles, jumping plant lice, grasshoppers and locusts. There have probably always been jumping insects and it has been suggested that this habit may have led to the evolution of flight in insects. It only required a jumping insect with flaps of cuticle on its thorax to be evolved and the first step towards true flight would have been taken. Fossil records suggest that this is what did happen.

▽ *Specimens of tiny springtails, some showing their unique forked jumping mechanism on the abdomen.*

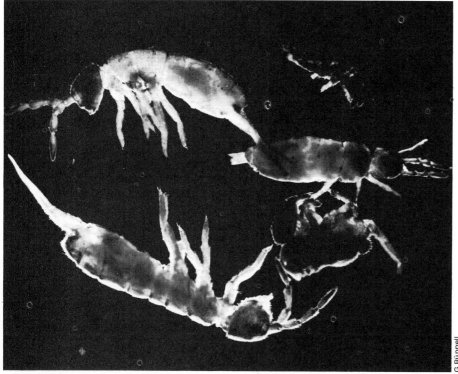

G Rüppell

Springtails are seldom more than $\frac{1}{5}$ in. long and they have two unique features. The first is a forkshaped 'spring' which is fastened to the hindend of the abdomen. It lies under the abdomen and is fastened with a catch, known as the hamula. When released from this catch, by a sudden forward movement, the fork strikes downwards and throws the springtail several inches into the air. The second feature is the ventral tube on the front end of the abdomen which was once thought to be a sucker-like or adhesive organ used by the springtail when climbing vegetation.

The 2 000 species are distributed all over the world, including the Arctic and the continent of Antarctica. Most of the species found in woodland litter are active

mushroom beds. *Tomocerus longicornis* attacks seedlings in greenhouses. *Podura aquatica* can be seen in hundreds on the surfaces of still pools, forming masses an inch across. *Anurida maritima* forms similar groups on the surfaces of rock pools on the shore. *Achorutes nivicola* lives on the surface of snow on glaciers, in the Arctic, and temporarily when snow lies in winter in temperate latitudes. *Entomobrya mawsoni* lives under stones in penguin rookeries on the Macquarie Islands in the subantarctic. Some springtails live in the nests of ants and termites. A noteworthy species is *Sminthurus viridis*, which is round and green and so small there may be 250 million of them, besides other springtails, in an acre of meadow in Britain. In Australia, where it has become a serious pest, the same species is known as the lucerne fly.

phylum	**Arthropoda**
class	**Insecta**
order	**Collembola**

Squat lobster

The four species of squat lobsters look like small lobsters but are more nearly related to hermit crabs. The body is stout and more flattened than in a true lobster and the broad abdomen is tucked under it. The antennae are long and slender, with a slightly stalked eye near the base of each. The long claws are strong and pointed, and the four pairs of legs all lack small pincers. Three pairs are used for walking, but the fourth pair is very small and weak and is usually tucked away out of sight. The largest **Galathea strigosa** is not more than 6 in. long in the body, and it is one of the more handsome crustaceans, being red marked with blue lines and dots. The claws and legs and the sides of the body bear numerous spines. The smallest **G. intermedia**, only 1 in. long including the claws, is also red marked with blue. Of the other two, both about 2 in. long, one **G. dispersa** is dull red, sometimes with pale markings, and the other **G. squamifera** is greenish-brown with red flecks.

All four species are European. The commonest **G. squamifera** is the dullest in colour and is the one most often found between tidemarks. The others are not common and live well down the shore, usually in shallow offshore waters.

Poor swimmers

Squat lobsters are crawlers but they can swim; they can dart backwards by stretching the abdomen backwards, and suddenly flicking it forwards. Whereas a lobster when alarmed will swim backwards for long distances, by alternately stretching and bending its abdomen, a squat lobster will not swim far but will try to crawl under the cover of rocks and pebbles. So, in its habits and in its structure, it represents an intermediate stage between the active true lobsters and crabs and the more sedentary hermit crabs. Squat lobsters are not difficult to find on rocky shores, especially in spring and summer, under large, flat stones. Their usual reaction on being discovered is to creep backwards, trying if possible to crawl away out of sight. The largest of them will try to use its claws in self-defence, but apart from this squat lobsters seem to lack the aggressive disposition characteristic of the true lobsters and crabs.

Particulate feeders

They can also be said to be intermediate in regard to their feeding habits. The larger of them will eat pieces of meat, when in aquaria, but this is unusual as they have lost the predatory habits typical of the larger crustaceans. Their usual food is made up chiefly of small particles of animal flesh which are swept into the mouth by a brushing action of the bristles on the mouth parts.

▽ Rock pool setting—an undeterred common squat lobster keeps company with a snakelocks anemone **Anemonia sulcata** and delicate red algae.

Jane Burton: Photo Res

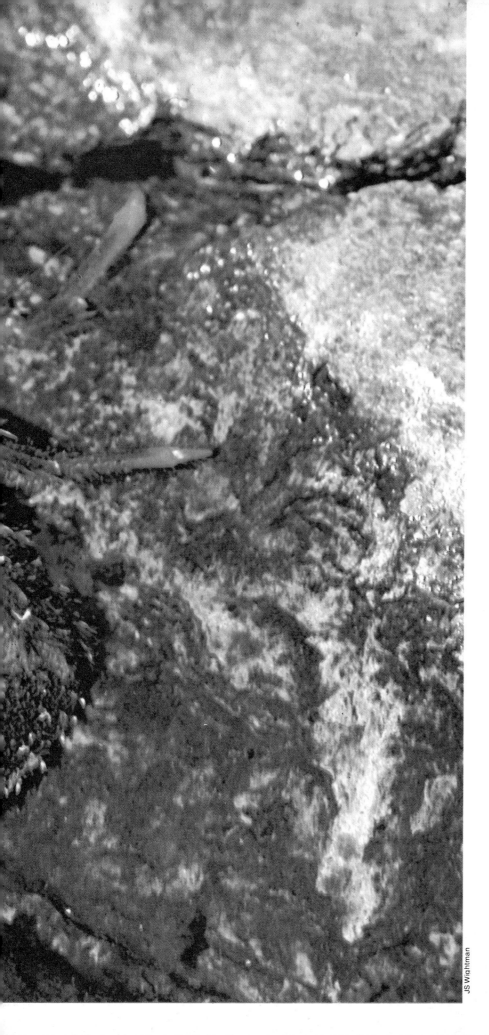

Primitive larvae

The life history is similar to that of other large crustaceans but the zoea larvae are more primitive and less highly specialized in their structure than are those of true crabs. They are more like those of shrimps and prawns. At a later stage in the larval life they look like very tiny but incomplete shrimps. The larvae of even the largest squat lobsters are only $\frac{1}{16}$ in. long.

Wayward crustaceans

The squat lobsters are not only some of the more fascinating crustaceans to watch; they are important for the light they shed on the relationships of the decapod (10-legged) crustaceans. On the one hand we have the shrimps, prawns, and lobsters, with the long abdomen normally fully extended backwards. On the other hand we have the true crabs with the abdomen small and tucked in under the rest of the body. In between we have the hermit crabs with an asymmetrical abdomen, with the legs much reduced and those on one side of the abdomen missing altogether. So at first sight the hermit crabs, while having quite obviously some relationship with shrimps, prawns, lobsters and crabs, are 'screwy' in shape and have gone off on a line of their own. They have also specialized in sheltering in empty shells.

If we could assemble all the squat lobsters and their relatives together we could build up a series showing how this came about. The abdomen of squat lobsters is slightly asymmetrical. That of the porcelain crab *Porcellana longicornis*, often found under stones in company with squat lobsters, has the abdomen slightly more asymmetrical. With luck we might find another relative nearby, the burrowing prawn *Callianassa subterranea*, which looks like a normal prawn but lives in a burrow in the sand and has one claw much larger than the other, as in hermit crabs. We might also find the stone crab *Lithodes maia*, which is spiny like the squat lobsters, looks like a spider crab, which is a true crab, but has a very asymmetrical abdomen.

The story is repeated with variations on other shores outside Europe. On the North American coasts, for example, there are the porcelain crabs *Pachycheles* and *Petrolisthes*, almost indistinguishable except to the expert eye from the European porcelain crab. There are also stone crabs *Lopholithodes*, sand crabs *Emerita* and mole crabs *Blepharipoda*, so named because they burrow. In these also we could trace the tendency towards asymmetry, the tendency to become particulate feeders rather than predators, the tendency to shelter in crevices, cracks or burrows, that have taken the hermit crab along its own evolutionary path.

phylum	**Arthropoda**
class	**Crustacea**
order	**Decapoda**
tribe	**Anomura**

◁ *The largest squat lobster **Galathea strigosa** is not more than 6 in. long in the body.*

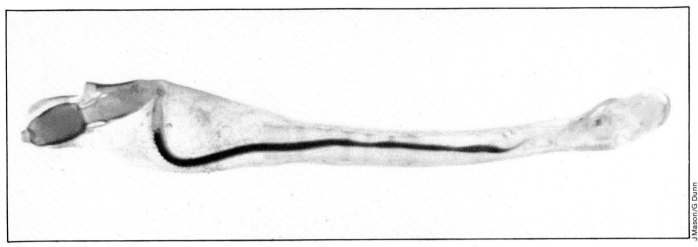

J Mason/G Dunn

Squid

All squids are marine, and in contrast to
their relatives, the octopuses and cuttlefish, they have a streamlined body and
are fast swimmers. There are about 350
species, ranging in size from less than an
inch to nearly 60 ft. The head bears two
well developed eyes, remarkably like our
own in structure though independently
evolved, eight arms corresponding to those
of an octopus, plus two longer tentacles.
The body tapers towards the rear, bears
lateral fins at the back and contains the
remains of the ancestral shell.

The underside of the body contains the
mantle cavity into which open the reproductive and excretory organs, the ink sac
and the hind end of the digestive tract.
Here also are the two gills in which the
squid's blue blood is oxygenated. The
pulsations of the muscular wall of the
mantle cavity continually draw water in
and out through a muscular funnel which
opens behind the head. The squid, like
other cephalopods, utilizes this water
current for jet propulsion, shooting it out
through the funnel which can be directed
forward or back to send the squid rapidly
in either direction. The water is sucked
in, not through the funnel, but around its
base. For the fastest possible response of
this system and for the synchronisation of
the contraction of the different muscle
fibres, rapidly-conducting nerve fibres are
essential in linking brain and muscle.
The nerve fibres of molluscs lack the
covering that facilitates the very rapid
conduction of nerve impulses in mammals,
but the rate at which nerve fibres can
conduct impulses increases with their
thickness. Thus squids have evolved
enormously thick nerve fibres to link
brain and mantle muscle. They are over
½mm thick as compared with diameters of
one thousandth to one fiftieth of a
millimetre in humans. Study of these
'giant fibres' has been of immense help
in elucidating the way in which nerve
impulses are conducted through the body
of an animal.

Heather Angel

△ **Loligo** spermatophore, a long torpedo-
shaped chitin tube containing spermatozoa.
During mating the male transfers bunches of
these spermatophores from his mantle cavity to
the female's mantle cavity using his specially
modified fourth arm (approx ×47).
◁ Beak of the squid **Loligo forbesi** removed
from the centre of the arms. The mouth's
parrot-like beak is sharp enough in some cases
to sever thick wires. Squid beaks are often
recovered in sperm whale stomachs. They give
useful information both on the distribution of
squid and the feeding habits of the whales.
▷ **Abraliopsis** with conspicuous light organs.
▽ Close-up of the suckers of one of the long
tentacles of **Loligo forbesi**. The hooked
marginal rings to the suckers aid in gripping
the prey. Both arms and tentacles bear suckers
though some of these, in 'hooked squids', are
replaced by hooks which act as 'claws'. They
cannot, however, be withdrawn.

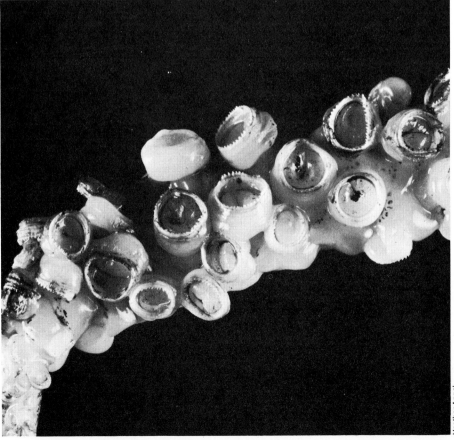

Heather Angel

△ *Moving backwards. The tentacles of these squid* **Loligo vulgaris** *are pointing to the left.*

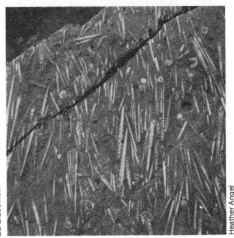

△ *Belemnites, fossil record of past squids.*

Illuminated squids

Squids tend to move about in shoals, often of one sex only. They can swim well in either direction but travel mostly backwards. Like the octopus (p 1604), they are masters of colour change and have chromatophores of various colours in the skin that can be contracted and expanded to produce a variety of patterns. *Sthenoteuthis*, for example, has chromatophores of the three primary colours—blue, yellow and red.

One of the best-known species is *Loligo forbesi* of the North Sea, northeast Atlantic and Mediterranean. Large ones may be 2 or 3 ft long, but most range from 8 to 12 in. Less typical in appearance is the small *Chiroteuthis veranyi* with its long tentacles many times the length of the body, and the reddish-purple to black *Histioteuthis* with six of its arms joined by a membranous web whose jellyfish-like movements largely replace the use of the funnel in swimming. In *Bathothauma*, a small deepsea squid, the arms are very short and are carried in a small rosette around the mouth on the tip of a long peduncle and the eyes are on long stalks. *Calliteuthis* also has unusual eyes in that one is much bigger than the other. The small one is surrounded by a circlet of light-producing organs. Many squids have light organs, especially those living in deep water. The light organs may be on the eyes, on the tentacles, or scattered all over the body. *Histioteuthis bonelliana* a Mediterranean species about a yard long, has nearly two hundred of them. The light organs themselves may be very complex, with reflectors, lenses, diaphragms, colour screens and other accessory structures. Some squids do not themselves produce the light but have luminescent bacteria in their light organs which are transmitted to the next generation in the squid's embryo. The light is sometimes given out from internal organs and shines through a translucent body wall.

The dreaded kraken

The largest squids belong to the genus *Architeuthis*, the biggest one known being a specimen of *A. princeps* stranded on the Newfoundland coast in 1878. Its body was 20 ft long and its total length 55 ft, a length only exceeded by a specimen of the less bulky *A. longimanus*, 57¼ ft long, found in Lyall Bay, New Zealand, in 1888. Smaller specimens of *Architeuthis* have been stranded on the shores of the British Isles. These giant squids, some of which probably exceed even the recorded maximum sizes, are no doubt responsible for the stories of the dreaded Kraken in Norse legend. From their anatomy they are thought not to be powerful swimmers and are believed to live at a depth of 600 – 1 200 ft.

Prey chased or ambushed

Fish and crustaceans are their main food, as well as smaller squids. Once seized, the prey is quickly paralysed by venom produced by one of the two pairs of salivary glands. *Loligo* seizes a fish behind the head and bites it off with its parrot-like beak; the rest is bitten into small pieces and digestion is completed in 4–6 hours. Squids may chase their prey or make use of their camouflaging abilities to ambush it.

Massive matings

In temperate seas squids generally breed in spring or summer. In *L. peali* of American waters, which is typical, courtship starts with the male displaying to a female with his arms. Coloured spots appear on his arms and he blushes red all over his body from time to time. His sperms are packed into special torpedo-shaped tubes of chitin about ⅜ in. long, called spermatophores, and he transfers bunches of these elaborate structures to the female by means of his left fourth arm which is specially modified for the purpose. Before doing so, he lies parallel to his mate, lower side to lower side and with his arms around her, just behind the head. He then takes some spermatophores from his own mantle cavity and places them in hers. Alternatively, the pair may join head to head, in which case the sperm packets are deposited on a glandular patch amongst the female's tentacles. The eggs are laid in strings of jelly material which become attached to the sea bed. *Loligo* seems to die after spawning. Courtship is a communal activity in squids and great shoals may gather for the purpose, sometimes then migrating inshore to breed. The number of eggs produced by a shoal may be colossal, though the egg masses of 40 ft or more across, reported off California in 1953 were exceptional. In 1955 it was estimated that in this locality the eggs covered 200 acres of seabed. The young hatch as recognizable squid-like forms.

Smoke screens save sometimes

Squids are too nimble to be netted in large numbers, except when they are gathered in mating shoals, but they are nevertheless not without enemies. They are eaten by petrels, albatrosses and other sea-birds and they are the main food of the king penguin. The emperor penguin also eats them in large numbers as do also seals, sea lions, elephant seals, toothed whales and tunny fish. For escape squids rely partly on their agility and excellent vision, but also on their ability to change colour and to blow ink out through the funnel. The ink may be used simply as a smoke screen, but in some species it remains for a while as a compact cloud in the water, roughly the size and shape of the squid producing it. As this decoy is formed, the squid darts off backwards, changing to a different and less conspicuous colour as it does so. The predator, presumably, tries to seize the blob of ink and loses sight of the squid itself.

Flying squids

There are at least two kinds of flying squids. Of these, *Onychoteuthis banksi* occurs in all oceans and is sometimes stranded on the shore. Its fins are wide and additional planes are provided by broad membranes on the arms. It was the account of the Kon-Tiki expedition that brought 'flying squids' to general attention, though they had long been known to sailors because they not uncommonly landed on the decks of ships. These extraordinary animals are hooked squids that can leave the water with such velocity that they may sail 50 – 60 yd through the air before re-entering the sea. They sometimes leap singly, sometimes in twos or threes. They have been known to hit ships as high as 20 ft above the waterline. This habit is probably a means of escape from predators.

phylum	**Mollusca**
class	**Cephalopoda**
order	**Dibranchia**
families	**Architeuthidae**
	Histioteuthidae
	Chiroteuthidae

Squirrelfish

Squirrelfishes are usually bright red and they have large eyes, giving them a faint resemblance to red squirrels, and this seems to be the only reason why they were given their common name. They have deep bodies compressed from side to side, large heads, strong jaws and large eyes. The largest is 2 ft long but 1 ft is a more usual length. Their scales are large with sharp points on their hind edges. There are sharp spines on the head and on the gill covers. The front half of the dorsal fin is spiny, the rear half tall and soft rayed. The anal fin has four spines in front, the middle one large. The large pelvic fins are situated forward on the body and level with the pectoral fins. The tailfin is forked. The red body is usually ornamented with silvery spots or stripes on the flanks, running from behind the gills to the base of the tailfin. One of the most widespread in the Indo-Pacific, the red soldierfish, lives in deeper water than most, down to 90 ft. It is bright red and each row of scales along its body bears a silvery stripe. Its fins are rosy with black markings.

There are 70 species in tropical seas throughout the world, most of them living in shallow water.

Unneighbourly fishes

Most squirrelfishes are nocturnal. By day they shelter singly in crevices and cracks in the coral. Each occupies a territory and shows a marked territorial behaviour. Some members of a related genus *Myripristis* contrast with typical squirrelfishes in sometimes forming shoals. Squirrelfishes are also noted for the noises they make, which are loud enough to be heard above the water. These are produced by the vibration of muscles attached to the swimbladder, which acts as a resonator. The sounds are used, it seems, for the same basic purpose as birdsong, to advertise the occupation of a territory and to bring pairs together for breeding. Their territorial instinct was made use of off the Hawaiian islands in fishing for squirrelfishes, which are an important food fish. A squirrelfish was caught, using a net, then a string was tied round the live fish which was put back into the water and dangled near the crevices in the rocks. The other fishes soon came out to fight it and, by drawing the captive fish gently to the surface, these could easily be caught by carefully lowering a net under them.

Prickly owls

Apart from their colour and the size of their eyes squirrelfishes are remembered because they are prickly to handle. They are also notable for their nocturnal habits, which are linked with the large size of their eyes. Indeed, they could more appropriately have been called owl fishes, except that the name squirrelfish was given them in the early 18th century when people were less interested in animal behaviour and more apt to give a name based upon general appearance. This, presumably, is what led to one species being called the wistful squirrelfish.

Staking out claims

They are predatory, catching smaller fishes, and one reason for their pronounced territorial instinct is that it keeps the individuals well spaced out, so avoiding competition with each other. This is probably when they use their sounds, to warn possible trespassers off their beat.

Helpless larvae

The connection between the sounds they produce and their breeding was first discovered by accident when squirrelfishes were in a display tank in a television studio in America. During the rehearsal the sounds were heard and a pair of squirrelfishes were seen to be courting, lying side by side with their tails pressed together and their bodies forming a V. From the eggs hatch larvae remarkable for their long pointed noses. The larvae swim to the surface and become part of the plankton. The larvae are dispersed by currents.

Hazards of infancy

Their nocturnal habits, spininess and their tendency to keep hidden probably means that squirrelfishes have relatively few enemies. The main dangers to the adults, especially those species which have fewer spines than average, is of being caught for human consumption. The chief dangers are in the larval stage when they are eaten in large numbers by tuna fishes.

▽ *In close formation, a small shoal of squirrelfishes* **Myripristis** *in the Red Sea, 20 ft down.*

G Mundey

Lights to their eyes

Squirrelfishes are said to be primitive because of certain details in their anatomy. They also form a link between the large multitude of perchlike fishes living today and certain kinds of fishes that were dominant during the Cretaceous period 135-70 million years ago, which had spiny rays on their fins. Even more primitive are the alfonsinos of the family Berycidae. These are also brightly coloured but differ in having a short rounded body and a long, fairly slender tail end. They also differ in living in deep water, at about 2 000 ft. The commonest species is the 2ft long *Beryx splendens* which is worldwide in warm seas and is fished commercially.

Another relative is the pinecone fish *Monocentris japonicus* of the family Monocentridae, only a few inches long, which has platelike spiny scales and lives in deep water in the tropical Indo-Pacific. It is eaten in Japan. The only other species in the family lives in Australian waters. It is *Monocentris gloriae-maris* (the glory of the sea — which shows what a beauty it is!). These not only have large wistful eyes but have two light organs under the lower jaw — pockets filled with luminescent bacteria.

Strangest of all are the related lantern-eyed fishes of the family Anomalopidae. None is more than a foot long. They also have large eyes with a light organ beneath each eye made up of tubes of luminous bacteria. The fish cannot control the light from the bacteria but they can cover it. Some species do this by drawing a blind — a kind of eyelid — over the light organ. In other species there is a muscle which turns the light organ round so its light is no longer visible from outside.

class	**Pisces**
order	**Beryciformes**
family	**Holocentridae**
genera & species	***Holocentrus rubrum*** *soldierfish* ***Holotrachys lima*** *wistful squirrelfish* *others*

▷ *Wide eyes, sharp spines and bright colours — characteristics of all squirrelfishes; the Hawaiian striped squirrelfish* **Holocentrus xantherythrus** *is no exception. Squirrelfishes are usually some shade of red but this species also sports candy stripes that look like strings of pearls. In comparison with* **Myripristis** *a schooling species (illustrated on the previous page)* **Holocentrus** *is a more solitary species and shows a strong territorial pattern. The Hawaiian striped squirrelfish is particularly renowned in that it was the first squirrelfish in which prenuptial activity was observed. A pair will hold their tails together, their heads apart, so that a V or Y is formed between them.*

H Hansen

Squirrel monkey

The small, slender South American squirrel monkey, with its small, almost human, white face and large dark eyes is known in German as Totenkopfaffe, or death's-head monkey. It has long thin hindlegs, rather shorter arms, and a short body. The head is rounded with a small face, and slightly protruding black muzzle. The nostrils, as in all South American monkeys, face sideways. The ears are rather pointed, with long white hairs directed out to the side. The tail is not prehensile, but tends to be held in a coiled position and often partly curls round something as a support. The tail is 16 in. long; the body is only 10 in. Squirrel monkeys have short, usually greenish fur, the top of the head being blue-black. All squirrel monkeys probably belong to a single species, although there is conspicuous variation in colour from one place to another. The Central American form has a jet black cap and the greenish colour of the body is overlaid with red, while two South American types, from Brazil and Peru respectively, are characterised as the 'Gothic' and 'Roman' squirrel monkeys, because the white arches above the eyes are said to resemble those particular architectural features!

In Central America, squirrel monkeys are found along the coastal strip on the Pacific side of the Panama isthmus. The same race extends down the Pacific coast of South America as far south as Ecuador. To the east of the Andes, they inhabit the tropical forest belt and much of the sub-tropical forest, extending from the Orinoco river, south across the Amazon, to the Mato Grosso region of Brazil, and possibly past the Llanos de Guarayos.

Loosely organised troops

Squirrel monkeys live in very large bands kept together by the females which lead the troop's movements and form a focus for the young and for the adult males. The males keep somewhat to the edges of the troop, having little to do with each other or the rest of the troop except in the mating season. Mutual grooming is very infrequent, and although some females are more influential than others, there is no marked hierarchy among them. There is more among the males but because of the low level of social organisation this is not really apparent except in the breeding season.

Squirrel monkeys are said to inhabit forest edge habitats and gallery forest, bordering large rivers, rather than closed primary jungle. They are very versatile ecologically, coming down to the ground and going up to the very tops of the trees. Their food consists of fruit, buds and insects, with little or no leaf matter. The tail, wrapped round a branch, is used as a stabiliser when feeding. It is wrapped around the body when a monkey is resting. The monkeys often rest in groups huddled together with their heads between their knees.

Each troop a matriarchy

The breeding season is not sharply defined but is a period of about five months during which both sexes undergo sexual development. There is a birth peak near the end of the season. The behaviour of all the males changes completely, as does their

△ *Games in the grass. Part of a troop of squirrel monkeys roll about on the ground. They move through the forest in loosely-knit troops of 12 – 100 individuals, advertising their presence with noisy twitterings.*
△▷ *A squirrel monkey, its long tail hanging as a balancer, sits alone in the tree tops.*

Squirrel monkey
(*Saimiri sciureus*)

appearance. They become much fatter in the arms, chest and head. They also become very vocal and highly aggressive, displaying to one another and chasing the females to mate with them. Mating reaches a peak in the dry season, and the young are born 170-180 days later, at the height of the rains. When a female is giving birth the others crowd round and watch the proceedings intently. The baby may be carried around by either male or female, but the male's interest is short-lived and the only thing that keeps him near the troop is the presence of the females. The baby can grip its mother's fur and stay clinging to her, even when it is asleep. Squirrel monkeys breed well in captivity and have been known to live for 21 years.

Discretion the better part

The defenceless squirrel monkey, because of its small size, falls easy prey to small cats, birds of prey, pythons and man. Their only defence is in flight. When one monkey gives an alarm call, the whole twittering troop falls silent. The males go to investigate the source of the disturbance, then return and lead the troop in the opposite direction away from any impending danger.

Monkey language

Many studies of squirrel monkeys' behaviour have been made. One group of scientists has concentrated on studying their use of sounds. They identified 26 separate calls made up of different combinations of a few basic sounds, known as peep, twit, ha, arr and shriek. Human language is also built up of basic elements, the number differing from one language to another. There are markedly fewer in the languages of the more primitive peoples and it is a reasonable assumption that they were fewer still in races of man long since extinct. So these studies provide one more link between monkeys and man. Another interesting point is that the vocalisations differ slightly as between the Gothic and the Roman types of squirrel monkeys.

class	**Mammalia**
order	**Primates**
family	**Cebidae**
genus & species	*Saimiri sciureus*

Starfish

No animal is more clearly symbolic of the sea than the starfish or sea star. Artists making drawings of sandy beaches seldom fail to include a starfish, yet a starfish lying on the shore is bound to be dead or dying. Starfishes are found in all seas. The typical form is made up of five arms radiating from a small central body with a toothless mouth on its underside. The number of arms may, however, be from 4 up to 50, and some of the common starfishes that normally have 5 arms may have from 3 to 7. The smallest starfishes are less than ½ in. across, the largest 3 ft. The commonest colours are yellow, orange, pink and red, but there are some starfishes that are grey, blue, green or purple. Some of the smallest, known as starlets or cushion stars, have very short arms, so their outline is pentagonal.

The body wall of a starfish is reinforced and supported by calcareous plates, or ossicles, more or less exposed at the surface but always with at least a thin covering of skin, although this may wear through in places. They may occur as closely set plates or form an open network. Spines of the same material project from the surface singly or in groups, each spine moved by muscles at its base. The surface may also bear many little pincer-like pedicellariae, like those of sea urchins (p 2091). The pedicellariae take various forms. Some consist of a pair of tiny jaws mounted on a short stalk while others consist simply of three spines with their bases close together. They play an important part, seizing small organisms, so preventing the surface becoming encrusted with algae and sedentary animals. The pedicellariae are aided by cilia distributed over the surface. The material of the ossicles, spines and pedicellariae of echinoderms is unique in the animal kingdom as each element is a single crystal of calcite growing in the form of a three-dimensional network, to combine both lightness and strength.

Besides a general covering of sensory cells there is a light sensitive 'optic cushion' at the base of a short tentacle, which is a modified tube-foot at the tip of each arm.

There are 2 000 species, most of which live in shallow seas but some live in deep seas. The species are most numerous in the northern part of the North Pacific.

▽ Not only rare but also beautifully symmetrical. This starfish **Archaster typicus** is the only one that shows anything approximating to copulation. Other starfishes merely release millions of eggs into the sea during the one breeding season of the year. ▽▷ A starfish can lose all its arms but one and still survive by using its efficient powers of regeneration. The top starfish is regenerating a third arm. As regeneration results in an increase in population it can be classed as a form of asexual reproduction.

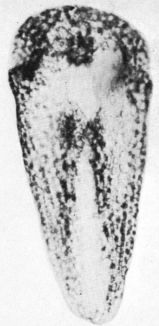
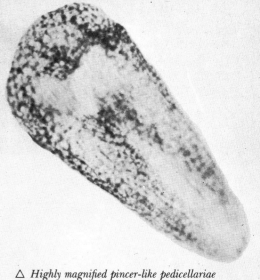

△ *Highly magnified pincer-like pedicellariae of* **Asterias**. *Lethal-looking contraptions, they help prevent the surface of the starfish from becoming encrusted with algae (× 230).*

One arm leads the way

Starfish move about by means of numerous tube-feet arranged in two or four rows along a groove on the underside of each arm. The tube-feet are hollow, muscular cylinders connecting at their bases with a system of tubes, the water vascular system which is filled with water. The 'feet' are pushed out hydraulically by the contraction of muscular sacs which lie at intervals along the system of tubes. At their tips there are usually suction discs, which also have sticky secretions which aid them in sticking to rock or prey. In the burrowing starfishes the tube-feet lack suckers. The water vascular system connecting the tube-feet opens to the outside through one or more porous plates on the upper surface. These madreporites, usually single, are situated off-centre of the body disc. In some species one arm nearly always takes the lead when the starfish is walking, but it is more usual for the arms to take turns in leading the way though there are differences in the extent to which each arm is favoured in a given species or individual. One species has been known to travel at the breath-taking speed of two yards a minute, but the more usual speeds are 2 – 3 in. a minute.

Multiplying by dividing

Irregular starfishes are sometimes found. They are those that have lost one or more arms and are regenerating new ones. Starfish have good powers of regeneration. They are also pests on oyster and mussel beds and those whose job it was to dredge the starfishes to get rid of them used to tear them apart and throw them back. This was a waste of time. The damaged starfishes merely grew from the torn parts, at least part of the body being necessary for regeneration. One genus *Linckia* is, however, known to be able to regenerate just from a piece of arm $\frac{1}{2}$ in. long. *Linckia* actually uses its arms to propagate itself – the arms pulling in two directions till the animal pulls itself in two. Any bits that get broken off add to the numbers of new individuals.

Protrusible stomach

Starfish are generally carnivorous, feeding on molluscs, worms, crustacea, fish and other echinoderms. Those, like *Asterias*, that prey on bivalves open them by arching over them and pulling on the shell valves with their tube-feet. The mollusc may resist for a long time, but the starfish eventually overwhelms it and the bivalve, due to muscle fatigue, has to allow its valves to part a little. The starfish then protrudes its stomach and inserts it inside out into the mollusc – a slit of $\frac{1}{10}$ mm is enough for it to make an entry. The stomach then secretes digestive enzymes into the mollusc. It has been said that the starfish gives out a poison to make the muscles of the mollusc relax. It now seems there is no firm evidence for this. The burrowing star, *Astropecten*, feeds differently, by taking food in whole. Shells or skeletons are later ejected through the mouth, for this genus has no anus. The cushion star *Porania pulvillus*, sometimes thrown up on the beaches of Europe, is unusual in that it feeds on microscopic organisms, propelling them towards its mouth by means of the cilia on its underside. Another species *Ctenodiscus crispatus* feeds on mud drawn into its mouth in strings of mucus along the grooves under the arms. *Asterina gibbosa*, one of the cushion stars, eats sponges and ascidians.

Born in a stomach

Both male and female starfish have two reproductive organs in each arm, each one opening by a pore at the base of the arm. There is usually one breeding season in a year, when millions of eggs may be released into the sea, *Asterias* may release 2 – 3 million within two hours, but as many as 200 million are released by some species. In *Asterias*, a bipinnaria larva hatches from the eggs. It has two circlets of cilia and is bilaterally symmetrical. The front end later becomes drawn out into three arms, the larva then being called a brachiolaria, while a curious asymmetrical development results in the growth of a young starfish mainly from the left side of the larva of which it still remains part. After about two months of drifting on currents with other plankton, the larva anchors itself by its three adhesive arms and the young starfish breaks free from the rest. Some cushion stars attach their eggs to the undersides of stones, the brachiolaria stage being omitted. The change into a starfish therefore occurs at an earlier stage of larval development. Several species brood their eggs and these hatch as young stars instead of as larvae. In these species, which mostly live in colder waters and particularly in the Antarctic, the eggs are large and yolky and less numerous. In some species, like the scarlet starfish *Henricia sanguinolenta*, the mother arches herself over her sticky eggs until they hatch. Meanwhile she goes without food. Amongst other methods of brooding, perhaps the oddest is that of *Leptasterias groenlandica* in which the eggs are kept in pouches in the parent's stomach.

Stars of the Sea

▷ *Cutting a swathe through the Pacific coral by eating all the live polyps, the crown of thorns starfish* **Acanthaster planci** *has now reached plague numbers. Its feeding habits create a vicious ascending reproductive cycle; where it has killed coral, beds of algae form—ideal sites for the starfish to lay more eggs.*

▽ *Madagascan starfishes* **Protoreaster lincki**, *a sea urchin and a hermit crab.*

▽▷ *A common starfish* **Asterias rubens** *demonstrates the suction power of its tube feet.*

▽▷▷ *Murky meeting: common starfishes of all shades and sizes congregate in a dark crevice, surrounded by green sponge.*

Gerald Cubitt

Edmund Hobson

Incredible story

Starfishes raid oyster and mussel beds and feed on the shellfish. These raids are, however, insignificant compared with the dramatic largescale destruction of coral reefs that has recently begun, which may have serious effects on fisheries and cause dangers of land erosion. The arch villain is the 'crown of thorns starfish' *Acanthaster planci*, so named for its covering of spines. It has 16 arms and averages 10 in. across, although it can reach two feet. It feeds on coral polyps. It was once thought a rarity—until about 1963 when swarms were reported on the Great Barrier Reef. At the same time it was implicated in the destruction of coral in the Red Sea. Now a population explosion is taking place in many widely separated areas of the Pacific and other oceans and it is killing off coral at an alarming rate. In 2½ years it killed nine-tenths of the coral along 38 kilometres of the shoreline of Guam. As the polyps are destroyed, the dead coral is overgrown with weed and most of the fish depart, their habitat ruined. The areas affected include the Great Barrier Reef of Australia, Fiji, Truck and Palau. Just why the crown of thorns is flourishing in this way is not clear though it is suspected that human interference is to blame, possibly through dredging or blasting.

phylum	**Echinodermata**
class	**Asteroidea**
order	**Phanerozonia**

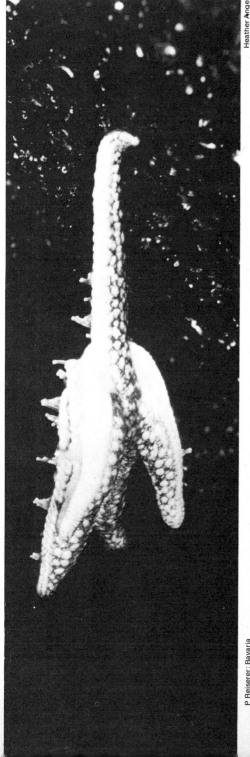

P Reiserer · Bavaria

Heather Angel

This Mediterranean stargazer, like other types, gets its name from the position of the eyes, which lie on the top of the head looking upwards.

SG Giacomelli

Stargazer

The stargazer is about as well equipped as any animal for getting an easy living and for beating off attacks on itself. It is also one of the ugliest of all fishes. Its head is large, broad and flat on top and the body, which is covered with small scales, tapers evenly from the head to the square-ended tailfin. Stargazers seldom exceed a foot in length, the largest being the northern stargazer of the Atlantic coast of the United States which reaches 22 in. The mouth is wide and the jaws are set almost vertical in bulldog-fashion. The wide set eyes on the top of the head gaze permanently upwards and behind each eye is a rhomboidal depression in the skin marking the position of the electric organs. The front dorsal fin is short and spiny, the second dorsal long and soft rayed, and the anal fin is long and soft like the second dorsal. The gill cover on each side is large, the pectoral fins are large and set low on the body and the pelvics are small and set under the throat. There are poison spines just above the pectoral fins, each having two grooves which carry poison from a gland at their base. The colour of the body is a dull brown which may be broken by whitish spots or stripes. In all cases the colours make the fishes incon-spicuous even on sand or mud.

There are more than 20 species which live in both shallow and deep waters, mainly in tropical and subtropical seas throughout the world.

Everything to protect itself

Stargazers bury themselves in sand or mud by a squirming side-to-side motion in which the large pectoral fins seem to act as shovels. Once buried they move about very little, lying with just the eyes and nostrils showing above the surface; in an emergency they can bury themselves temporarily to a depth of one foot. In most stargazers the nostrils open into the mouth, which is unusual in fishes, and water is drawn in through them to pass across the gills. The lips are fringed with short fleshy tentacles which may act as a filter to keep out sand.

Their electric organs can generate 50 volts, enough to make anyone touching them throw the fish aside and wonder what has happened. They are formed of modified eye muscles each of the electroplates repre-senting a single muscle fibre. The poison spines are a second form of defence and there are reports of fatal accidents to humans although Caras in *Dangerous to Man* states he could find no evidence for this.

Mediterranean stargazer with worm-like lure.

Chris Howell-Jones

Feeding by fair means or foul

Any small animals swimming near the star-gazer's mouth, with its opening more or less level with the surface of the mud, is snapped up. These include small crusta-ceans and worms, as well as small unwary fishes. Stargazers also have a worm-like fleshy filament fastened under the tongue just inside the mouth that can be pushed out and waggled to arouse the curiosity of larger fishes, drawing them nearer the mouth, to be snapped up.

Normal infancy

Although they do not normally move about much there seems to be some migration, probably linked with temperature. Star-gazers sometimes move into shallow tem-perate seas in summer, for example. They also apparently swim into deeper water for spawning. Until they are about an inch long the baby stargazers have the normal shape of young perch-like fishes with eyes at the sides of the head and mouth horizontal. Then, as the head flattens and the eyes move up, certain muscles of the eye change to form the electroplates.

Fair flavoured fish

The stargazers sometimes appear under the scientific name *Astroscopus*, meaning liter-ally to look at the stars. Others are called *Uranoscopus*, looking at the heavens, which amounts to the same thing. The Mediter-ranean stargazer, which was known to the Ancient Greeks and Romans, and was the first stargazer to be given a scientific name, carries the specific name *scaber* meaning rough, scurvy or untidy. It is an apt des-cription of its appearance, and should be enough to put off anyone trying to prepare it for the table, yet stargazers are relished in several parts of the world. M Constantin-Weyer, who wrote *The Private Life of Fishes*, assures us that the stargazer is delicious, at least in a *bouillabaisse*.

class	**Pisces**
order	**Perciformes**
family	**Uranoscopidae**
genera & species	***Astroscopus guttatus*** *northern stargazer* ***Uranoscopus scaber*** *Mediterranean stargazer others*

*A green array of glossy starlings **Lamprocolius** decorate a tree in Ethiopia; African starlings are generally brilliantly coloured.*

Starling

Taken as a family the starlings are highly successful but none can compete with the success story of the common starling. It is 8½ in. long with a stout body, a short tail and broad, pointed wings. Its plumage changes markedly throughout the year. Young starlings are brown and in their first autumn they moult to a spotted plumage with a brown head. At the same time the adults have light spots on a dark ground with a green iridescence, the spots of the female being bolder than those of the male. By the spring the spots are gone, due to the abrasion of the ends of the feathers, and all adults are then blackish, with iridescence. The bill is quite long and horn coloured in winter, yellowish in spring and summer. The changes are confusing but when its plumage is at its best the common starling is a handsome bird. So also are its relatives. The rosy pastor of eastern Europe and Asia has a pink body, a dark-crested head, and dark wings and tail. The glossy starlings of the South Pacific are greenish-black as adults but are heavily streaked with white when young. The oxpecker (p 1653) or tickbird and the mynahs (p 1552) are also included in the 110 species of Old World birds which make up the family. Some, like the African wattled starling, have further ornamentations. It moults its head feathers in the breeding season and grows long wattles.

Living clouds

Starlings tend to live in flocks and this is most marked in the common starling. During the day the flock spreads out for feeding but in the late afternoon all the starlings in the neighbourhood begin to come together for roosting. The pattern of behaviour then varies. Typically, the birds begin to gather in small groups of 12—20, on bushes or in trees. Each group later joins a nearby group and the process of forming larger and larger groups continues until a flock thousands strong is formed which flies around and around, spreading out and coming together, like a huge smoke cloud in the sky.

Orderly roosting formations

Sometimes a flock of several hundreds will fly in formation, turning, wheeling and changing course with almost military precision. At other times the birds will make direct for the roost in small groups of twos or threes or up to a dozen. There are times when starlings will gather in trees in a noisy

*A wattled starling—**Creatophora cinerea**.*

chorus, the well-known murmuration. Then suddenly, as if cut by a knife, the chorus stops and a few seconds later all the birds take to the wing and fly off. As they fly away the last five or six birds return to the tree and start singing again. Other starlings fly in all directions until 40—50 have assembled and a chorus builds up again. Then suddenly it ceases again, as if cut off with a knife and a few seconds later they all fly off in the same direction as the previous group, again a few birds detaching themselves from the rear and returning to the tree. The whole ceremony is re-enacted, perhaps six times, before all the starlings in the surrounding area have assembled and flown to the roost.

Nuisance in towns

In rural areas starlings roost in a clump of trees, fouling the ground beneath with their droppings, or in a church tower in a village. This was the pattern of their roosting everywhere until the 1890's, when they started to roost in towns. The first record in London was in 1894. Today there are two large dormitories, one centred on St Paul's cathedral, the other around Trafalgar Square. Every night, except in the breeding season, a vast flock assembles in these places, the individual birds perching on ledges and window sills for the night. On one occasion starlings settled in such numbers on the big hand of Big Ben they stopped the clock. Starlings roosting on buildings have now become a regular feature, especially in the larger towns. Many methods of driving them away have been tried, to save the buildings being fouled by their droppings, but they have all met with indifferent success.

Colonizing America

The common starling, native to most of Europe and western and central Asia, has been taken to Australia and New Zealand and to North America. Their most spectacular spread has been in America. Several unsuccessful attempts had been made to introduce them to the United States and Canada. Then in 1890 sixty were released in a New York park, and forty more in 1891. By 1948 they had spread all across the United States and reached the Pacific coast. They have now spread to Canada and Mexico.

Mainly beneficial to agriculture

In the 1920's a panel was set up in the United States to assess the effect of starlings on agriculture. Its report showed that starlings are beneficial because of what they eat and this slightly outweighs their nuisance

2207

value in other ways, such as fouling the ground under their roosts and raiding soft fruits. For most of the year starlings probe the grassland and ploughed fields with their beaks for insect grubs, especially for the troublesome wireworm. They also feed among cattle, taking insects disturbed by their hoofs. At other times they take soft fruits and in autumn and winter they feed on berries, gorging themselves as long as a particular crop of berries lasts, whether elder, yew or rowan.

Selfish nesters

Most starlings nest in holes in trees. The Celebes starling, which has a bill like a woodpecker, excavates its own cavities in trees. The common starling also nests in holes in buildings and in roofspaces, and will often drive other birds out of suitable nesting cavities. Breeding begins in April, the male building the nest, of leaves and dry grass, the female lining it. The eggs, 4—9 in a clutch, are very pale blue, sometimes with small red spots. They hatch in 12—13 days, the female incubating them at night, the two sharing the incubation by day. The fledglings are fed by both parents for 3 weeks. Starlings more than most birds tend to lay occasional eggs on the ground. Polygamy has been recorded, with one male mating with three females and helping each of them with the incubation and feeding of the fledglings.

Success against enemies

Much of the success of starlings, in building up large populations and in spreading over

▽ *Starling sequence: four common starlings perch on a branch in their white spangled winter plumage. At other times of the year the plumage is iridescent purple, green and blue. They are gregarious birds forming large flocks to roost. This has led to their becoming unpopular in large towns and cities where they congregate on window ledges and the upper parts of buildings which they foul with their droppings. They also make a lot of noise, their high-pitched squealings rising over the noise of the traffic. It is a pity that this attractive bird has become a pest.*

new areas is due to their adaptability in using nesting sites, their wide diet and their own pugnacity—they will drive other birds from feeding tables. It is also due to the close-knit family life: starlings more than most birds seem to control and marshal their young, especially in times of danger. Attacks by birds of prey on flocks of adults are largely thwarted by the starlings flying in tightly packed box formations as soon as the enemy is spotted.

Sounds that deceive

Starlings are very vocal, but besides their native calls many are proficient mimics of the calls of other birds or of mechanical sounds. When a gull or curlew is heard calling and neither can be seen, it is likely to be a starling on the roof-tops imitating their calls. Once, when the fountain in the garden of an English house had been turned off, the tinkle of falling water could still be heard; it was traced to a starling. Of the many records of their mimickings perhaps the most remarkable followed some tree-felling. A power-driven saw was being used to fell the trees. After this had been going on for a few days a starling was seen one midday, a quarter of a mile from the wood, while the woodmen were having their lunch, making the sounds of a distant power-driven saw. It followed this with a medley of sounds which made no sense until the listener realized it was the sound of a falling tree, with the swish of the twigs, the rustle of leaves, and the final crashing sounds as the limbs and trunk hit the ground.

class	**Aves**
order	**Passeriformes**
family	**Sturnidae**
genera & species	***Aplonis metallica*** *glossy starling* ***Sturnus roseus*** *rosy starling* ***Scissirostrum dubium*** *Celebes starling* ***Sturnus vulgaris*** *common starling, others*

John Markham

Steamer duck

The three steamer ducks are massive, ungainly birds that live in southern South America. The body is very heavy, weighing up to 14 lb in the largest species, the feet are large and the bill very broad. The wings are short and two species are unable to fly. The Magellan flightless steamer duck is the largest of the three. Males weigh 12—14 lb and the females a few pounds less, but otherwise the sexes are very similar. The plumage is mottled grey. The head and neck are grey mottled with white, the crown is bluish-grey and there is a brownish tinge on the throat. It lives on the coasts of South America from Concepcion in Chile to Cape San Diego in Argentina, including the islands around Tierra del Fuego. The Falkland Islands flightless steamer duck is confined to the Falkland Islands where it is known as the logger duck. It is rather smaller than the Magellan species and the sexes have similar plumage. Both have darker bodies than the Magellan steamer duck and have a yellow ring around the neck. Females have a dark head with a white stripe running back from the eye while males have a paler grey head.

The flying steamer duck, the smallest of the three, with the males weighing about 6 lb, is found both in the Falkland Islands and in southern South America, from Valdivia in Chile and Puerto Deseado in Argentina south to Tierra del Fuego. The flying steamer duck has longer wings and tail than the flightless species and its legs are more slender. Its plumage is darker, being almost brown over most of the body and the male can be distinguished by a whitish head. All the steamer ducks have white patches on their wings which can be seen when the wings are folded.

Tame wild ducks

Steamer ducks are so-called because of their habit of 'steaming' over the water, rushing across the surface propelled by their wings and legs and throwing up sheets of spray. The flying steamer duck can fly well but prefers to 'steam' if disturbed. The Magellan steamer duck has been recorded as 'steaming' at 8 mph over short distances when chased by a boat. The flightless steamer ducks are confined to coasts and are rarely seen in fresh water except to drink and bathe. The flying steamer duck, on the other hand, regularly inhabits lakes and rivers. Coastal steamer ducks are rarely seen more than a few hundred feet from land and the Magellan steamer duck is not found on the parts of the South American coast where there are extremely large tides.

In the Falkland Islands where steamer ducks have few, if any, enemies, they are remarkably tame, as so often occurs with animals living on islands where there are no predators. In Port Stanley, the only town in the Falkland Islands, flightless steamer ducks live on the beach just below the main road. They take little notice of passing people and, in turn, are no more molested than the domestic duck on a village pond.

Fond of small shellfish

Steamer ducks feed on aquatic animals which they catch by diving in shallow water. The diet is mainly molluscs but also includes crustaceans, although the flying steamer duck with its smaller bill eats fewer thick-shelled molluscs than the others.

Father stands guard

In their breeding behaviour steamer ducks show several similarities to the shelducks (p 2117), to which they may be related. They mate for life and the male vigorously defends the territory, not only against other steamer ducks but also against other birds, including other kinds of ducks, penguins and geese. Battles between male steamer ducks may be very violent. They swim towards each other sinking lower and lower into the water, so when they meet they are almost submerged. They fight by grabbing each other's heads and beating with their wings which bear yellow knobs.

The 4—10 eggs are laid in a nest near the shore and are incubated by the female while the male keeps watch, either from the shore or from the water. Shortly after the chicks have hatched the female leads them to the water. They stay near the female but the male is always nearby and comes to the female's assistance if the brood is molested by gulls or skuas. Some chicks, however, fall prey to these birds.

Tough bird

As with other flightless birds steamer ducks have been able to develop a much heavier, stronger body than the fragile light bodies necessary in flying birds. A thick skull seems to be essential for the male steamer ducks to be able to survive the battering they give each other. Blood is regularly drawn in these fights and many males bear the scars of past battles. The extreme toughness of the Falkland steamer duck was demonstrated by the American ornithologist Olin Pettingill Jr, who spent some time in the Falkland Islands. He wanted to collect some steamer ducks for a museum collection but when he discharged a 12-bore shotgun at close range, his target merely walked away. Eventually a very heavy charge had to be used and when skinning the duck, Pettingill had to use a saw to cut through the skull.

class	**Aves**
order	**Anseriformes**
family	**Anatidae**
genus & species	***Tachyeres brachypterus*** *Falkland Island flightless steamer duck*
	T. patagonicus *flying steamer duck*
	T. pteneres *Magellan flightless steamer duck*

Grounded pair: Falkland Island flightless steamer ducks stand huddled in shallow water.

Philippa Scott

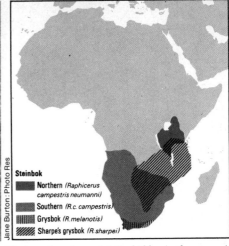

Steinbok
- Northern (*Raphicerus campestris neumanni*)
- Southern (*R. c. campestris*)
- Grysbok (*R. melanotis*)
- Sharpe's grysbok (*R. sharpei*)

Its senses alerted, a steinbok stares towards the camera before deciding if danger is imminent. Instead of fleeing when alarmed it lies hidden in the grass with its neck outstretched. The map shows the discontinuous distribution of the four types of steinbok; the species have definite boundaries between each other.

Steinbok

The steinbok is a dainty antelope with large eyes and ears, which makes it very appealing. With its relative the grysbok, it is closely related to the oribi (p 1629) and the suni. The steinbok and grysbok are, like the suni, 20 in. or less in height and have a coarse, rough coat. The males have simple spiky horns. Where the oribi and the suni have ribbed horns set at an angle to the vertical, the steinbok and grysbok have smooth upright horns. Like the suni, they lack the knee-tufts and the bare patch under the ear of the oribi, the tail is short and not bushy and the underparts are white. The male has a small gland in the groin, and both sexes have a rounded gland $\frac{1}{2}$ in. in diameter, $\frac{1}{8}$ in. deep in front of the eyes.

The steinbok is a uniform reddish or greyish fawn and has no lateral hoofs, just the small subsidiary hoofs which many antelopes have, above and behind the main one. The two species of grysbok are smaller and have white-speckled coats and longer ears. The ordinary grysbok has small lateral hoofs and is deep rufous, while Sharpe's grysbok is tawny rufous with no lateral hoofs. In Sharpe's grysbok, as opposed to the other two, the face-gland is surrounded by very short hairs; in the other two it is surrounded by a large area of naked skin.

The steinbok has a discontinuous distribution: the southern race is found from southernmost Africa, except for the southeast coast, north as far as the Zambesi and southern Angola. The northern race, which is paler with white rings round the eyes, is found in western Tanzania and as far north as southwestern Kenya. The grysbok is found in the coastal region of the southwest Cape, as far east as 28° E. Sharpe's grysbok is found from Natal and Transvaal north into Tanzania, reaching as far north as 2° 30′ S in the west of Tanzania.

Hermits of the bush

Steinbok and grysbok both live in scrub and bush country wherever there is sufficient undergrowth for them to hide. By day they lie up in the grass, or in old aardvark holes, only emerging at dawn and dusk to feed and move about. They are usually solitary. The most seen together at one time is three, probably a mated pair with their most recent young. Each individual—or pair, when two do come together—occupies a territory. Whether this is actually defended is not known, but the occupant does not appear to wander outside it, once the territory is established. The territory is marked by dung-heaps, which have the owner's scent on them and are scattered at points around the territory.

Ceremonial courtship

The female steinbok comes into season every three months, for about four days at a time. When she does, the male becomes very aggressive. The pair rub their faces together, exchanging secretions from their face glands, like duikers (see p 673). The courtship ceremony also includes a leg-beat, or Laufschlag (see p 1635). Gestation is 210 days; the female lies down to give birth, and in the wild it seems that birth usually takes place in a disused aardvark burrow. There is a birth peak in November and December, at least for the southern steinbok; more often twins are born rather than a single young.

Young Sharpe's grysbok were recorded to be 10 in. high at 20 days and to weigh 2–3 lb; this is somewhat more than half the adult height and a quarter of the adult weight—in fact a large youngster for such a small antelope.

Differing tactics

Leopards, cheetahs, jackals and hawks are probably the most dangerous predators of these little antelope. The grysbok's usual response to danger is to lie hidden in the grass with outstretched neck. If it is seen, it scuttles swiftly away with its head straight out in front. The steinbok moves with more of a gallop, and it holds its head higher as it runs. When cornered, it often puts up a fight, butting with its head and striking out viciously with its hoofs.

Cousins under the skin

The dwarf antelopes include the steinbok and grysbok, the suni, oribi, dikdik, beira, klipspringer and probably the Vaal rhebok. They are very closely related to one another and belong to the Neotragini tribe of antelopes. They all agree in being very small, with dark uppersides and white undersides, in having simple spiky horns, glands in the face and on the knees and in various other characters. The largest is the somewhat aberrant rhebok *Pelea capreolus* which is 30–31 in. high. The oribi and beira may reach 28 in., but normally none is above 20 in. high. Some are rather divergent in appearance: the rhebok has thick rabbity fur and a swollen, glandular muzzle; the klipspringer has a peculiar pithy fur and high, truncated hoofs for rock-climbing; the dikdiks all have inflated noses and tufted crowns. This leaves the steinbok, suni, oribi and beira which are rather more closely related to one another and have perhaps rather intricate points of difference between them. They are, however, distinguished by behavioural characteristics as much as anything else, such as the gazelle-like 'stotting' or 'pronking' of the oribi and its extended gallop; the swift smooth run, after initial hiding, of the steinbok and grysbok; the dodging and twisting avoidance behaviour of the suni; and the wariness and agility of the beira. In courtship, too, there are differences, such as the male pushing his head under the female's hind-quarters in the oribi, or the facial rubbing of the steinbok; but the 'Laufschlag' or leg-beat is a common feature of all the dwarf 'antelopes', and shows that they are closely related to the gazelles. All the dwarf antelopes, except perhaps the beira, seem to be territorial and live in pairs.

class	**Mammalia**
order	**Artiodactyla**
family	**Bovidae**
genus & species	***Raphicerus campestris campestris*** southern
	R. c. neumanni northern
	R. melanotis grysbok
	R. sharpei Sharpe's grysbok

Curious steppe lemmings investigate the heather. A distinctive feature of the laboratory species is a dark stripe along the back.

Steppe lemming

The steppe lemming has the doubtful honour of displacing the traditional guinea pig as a laboratory animal. In North America it is called the sagebrush vole and it combines the characters of lemmings and voles. The steppe lemming is a stocky rodent 3½–4 in. long with a tail one inch long. It has the blunt muzzle and the small ears and eyes of a vole, and its face is covered with numerous very long whiskers. Its long, soft fur is grey to sandy in colour with the underparts buff to silvery white, and in the laboratory species there is a dark strip along the back. The legs are short, the toes have stout claws and the soles of the feet are hairy.

*There are three species: **Lagurus lagurus,** the laboratory species, ranging from southern Russia to western Siberia, Kazakhstan and Dzungaria; **L. luteus** of Chinese Turkestan to Mongolia; and **L. curtatus** of southwestern Canada and the western United States.*

Frugal grass eaters

Unlike the related rodents, the lemmings and voles, steppe lemmings live mainly in semi-deserts and dry steppes where grass is sparse, but they may also move into pastures and arable land. They are mainly nocturnal, only occasionally being seen by day, and they are active the year round. They live in loose colonies making short burrows each consisting of several tunnels with a number of entrances and several nesting chambers. Most desert rodents eat mainly seeds but the steppe lemming feeds chiefly on green plants. So long as there is plenty of green food they need not drink. Laboratory animals do best on grass and hay with thin twigs of willow, seeds, grain and a limited amount of root vegetables, such as carrot and beet. If given too rich a diet they become overweight and the breeding rate drops.

Unintentional haymakers

Steppe lemmings do not move far from their burrows and in summer, when grass is most plentiful, wherever they feed they leave some of the grass lying on the ground. Some individuals, about 1 in 10, take this hay litter into their burrows to store as food. The rest of the colony use this store in winter when supplies are short, taking it as and when needed. Wasteful feeding and hoarding food are common among rodents. Yet there are a few animals, such as the pika (p 1757), that can be said actually to make hay. The steppe lemmings may perhaps be in process of acquiring the habit.

Large infant turnover

Steppe lemmings make their nests of plant fibres. The American sagebrush vole breeds all the year round. The Asiatic species has up to five litters during summer. The gestation period is 20–22 days, 24–26 days in the American species, and there are usually 4–10 young in a litter. Nursing females—unusual among rodents—are very tolerant of each other and often live together when they have litters. In the laboratory a pair may have 10–12 litters a year. The babies weigh $\frac{1}{20}$ oz at birth. This is doubled in 5 days and doubled again in 12 days, by which time the eyes have opened and the babies have begun to feed themselves.

They are fully weaned 5–6 days later. The females are sexually mature at 60 days, the males at 60–75 days. The life-span is 2–2½ years, with a maximum of 3 years.

Ideal 'guinea pigs'

Steppe lemmings *L. lagurus* were first bred in the laboratory 30 years ago in the USSR and in the early 1960's colonies were established in Germany and England for research on diseases such as turalaemia and poliomyelitis. It was then realized that the species has only a small number of chromosomes and the individual chromosomes are easily distinguished. The lemmings are therefore an asset in the study of genetics and especially the genetics of cancer. The advantages, from the laboratory point of view, are that the animals are small, easy to feed and maintain, do not hibernate, are easily tamed, are docile in nature, and have no unpleasant odour. Moreover, they breed rapidly and grow quickly, so there is a quick turnover in terms of individuals. In their rapid succession of generations steppe lemmings have something of the advantages of the fruit flies *Drosophila* as regards genetical research and they are smaller than guinea pigs and therefore require less space—which is hard luck on steppe lemmings.

class	**Mammalia**
order	**Rodentia**
family	**Cricetidae**
genus & species	*Lagurus lagurus* others

Incredible birth: this **Bactrododema aculiferum** *has just hatched from its tiny egg shell, having first pushed off the top of the egg, the operculum.*

Stick-insect

Stick-insects are today more commonly kept as pets than probably any other insect. They are sluggish and live among the foliage of trees and bushes or in low-growing herbage, relying for protection on their resemblance to their surroundings. They are always long and very slender, usually with smooth bodies, although some species are spiny. The larger kinds look like twigs and may be green or brown; the small species and the young of the larger ones are usually green and resemble the midribs of leaves or the stems and blades of grass. Some are very large and the Asian species **Palophus titan** *is the longest living insect, sometimes exceeding a foot in length.*

Some stick-insects have wings but many are wingless, a condition that enhances their resemblance to twigs.

Stick-insects, with the leaf-insects, comprise an order, the Phasmida, once included in the Orthoptera together with the grass-hoppers, mantids, cockroaches and others, but this group has now been divided into several separate orders. About 2 000 species of phasmids are known, the majority being found in the Oriental tropics. One species, **Bacillus rossii,** *is native to Europe, ranging as far north as central France. Two kinds of stick-insects from New Zealand have become established in the extreme southwest of the British Isles: the prickly stick-insect* **Acanthoxyla prasina** *in Devonshire and on Tresco in the Scilly Isles, and the smooth stick-insect* **Clitarchus hookeri** *also on Tresco and on an island off County Kerry, Eire. The so-called laboratory stick-insect* **Carausius morosus** *is an Oriental species often kept in schools and laboratories and more generally as a pet. It is a very easy insect to keep and breed and can be fed on leaves of privet, ivy or lilac. It cannot, however, survive out of doors through the cold winter in northern Europe and must be kept inside.*

Dazzle and hide

Most stick-insects feed and move about only at night. By day they remain motionless and often appear to be 'feigning death'. In fact they pass into a hypnotic or catalyptic state during the day. When they are in this condition the limbs can be moved into any position and will stay there, rather as if the joints were made of wax. Some of the winged species are active by day. In many of these the hindwings—which are the only ones developed for flying—are brightly coloured but are entirely concealed when the insect is at rest. If it is disturbed the wings are suddenly unfolded and the resultant flash of bright colour is confusing to a searching predator. Then, when the wings are closed again, the bright colour suddenly disappears, so the exact position at which the insect has alighted is effectively concealed. This is a well-known protective device and is called 'flash coloration'.

All stick-insects are plant eaters and occasionally they become numerous enough to defoliate areas of woodland. In Australia there are two species which occur in swampy areas but also feed on agricultural crops where they sometimes cause serious damage.

Eggs like raindrops

All the phasmids lay rather large, hard-shelled eggs which look very like seeds. In some cases they closely resemble the actual seeds of the plant on which the insect feeds. The eggs are dropped by the females at random. The tap of falling eggs is often heard from the cages of captive stick-insects and a North American species *Diapheromera femorata* is sometimes so numerous that the sound of thousands of its eggs falling on the forest floor is as loud as that of rain.

Several hundred eggs are usually laid, a few each day, and they take a long time to hatch. Those of the laboratory stick-insect hatch in 4—6 months at ordinary room temperatures, but this can be speeded up to 2 months by extra warmth or retarded to 8 months by cold conditions such as an un-heated room in winter. The eggs of the Madagascar stick-insect *Sipyloidea sipylus* will hatch in as little as one month if kept at $24°C/75°F-27°C/80°F$, but at lower temperatures may lie dormant for up to a year.

The young look very like the adults in all except size and, in the case of the winged species, in lacking wings, which develop gradually during growth.

Many stick-insects reproduce by partheno-genesis, that is the females lay fertile eggs without mating. In these species the males are usually rare; in cultures of the laboratory stick-insect, for example, they number about one in every 4 000 females. Of the two New Zealand species already mentioned, the male of the prickly stick-insect is un-known and possibly does not exist. In New Zealand, males of the smooth stick-insect are almost as common as females, but no males have been found in the small British colonies of the same species and the eggs develop without fertilisation.

2213

Odd colours

The laboratory stick-insect occurs in various colour forms ranging from green to shades of brown. The colour is determined by green, brown, orange-red and yellow granules in the cells of the surface layer of the skin. Pure green individuals cannot change colour, but the others regularly change, becoming darker at night and paler by day. The change is brought about by movement of the pigment granules within the cells. Brown pigments may move to the surface and spread out, making the insect dark in tone, or they may contract into lumps and move to the inner part of the cell so the insect becomes pale. The orange-red granules can also move about in this way, but not the green and yellow ones.

The alternation of colours becomes established by exposure to normal day and night, but once established it continues as a rhythm governed by the time cycle of 24 hours. A stick-insect conditioned to normal light change and then kept in permanent darkness will continue for several weeks to change colour every 24 hours, just as it did before. If it is kept in the dark by day and exposed to artificial light at night a reversed rhythm will develop in response to these conditions. This also persists for some time when the insect is kept continually in darkness with no light at all.

A Bannister: NHPA

phylum	**Arthropoda**
class	**Insecta**
order	**Phasmida**
families	**Bacteriidae**
	Phasmidae

△ *Remarkable camouflage: head of* **Bactrododema aculiferum** *with its ear-like projections looking very like broken-off twigs.*
▽ *Precarious upside-down mating of* **Gratidia** *spp. The female holds onto the stem as the male clasps her — both beautifully camouflaged.*
▷ *Rare shot: 7-inch* **Clemancatha regale.**

A Bannister: NHPA

Stickleback

Sticklebacks are not just tiny fishes or tiddlers caught by small boys with a bent pin on a line. They were used in some of the earliest modern studies of animal behaviour, and today they are used in testing for polluted water.

All sticklebacks have a long body, large head and strong jaws. They range in size from 2½ — 7½ in., most being only 3 — 4 in. long. The colour is usually greenish to black on the back and silver on the belly, sometimes with dark bars on the sides. They have two dorsal fins the first of which is made up of well spaced spines. The anal fin is similar to the second dorsal and lies opposite it. Each pelvic fin is one long spike and the pectoral fins are large. Most sticklebacks have a series of bony plates along each flank, the number varying with the species, and also within the species according to temperature and salinity.

There are a dozen species in the north temperate zone of the northern hemisphere and two of them range across Europe, Asia and North America. They are tolerant of salty water, at least two being found in the sea as well as in freshwater and two are wholly marine.

At home in river or sea

The 3-spined stickleback or tiddler, the most widespread, and the one we are most concerned with here, occurs throughout the northern hemisphere. It lives in all fresh waters except fast flowing mountain streams. It is also found in estuaries and along the coasts, and it has been caught 2—3 miles out at sea. It is not often found in stagnant or weed-choked waters, where the 10-spined stickleback, also known as the 9-spined, can live. Its distribution is similar to that of the 3-spined but is more local, both in North America and Eurasia. The 15-spined is wholly marine. In North America the 2½ in. brook stickleback is found in the fresh waters of the United States and Canada, and the 4-spined stickleback is common along the eastern seaboard, from Virginia to Nova Scotia.

Swarms of sticklebacks

There is a remarkable occurrence recorded by Thomas Pennant in the mid-18th century. He tells us that in the Welland river, in eastern England, sticklebacks could be seen in 'such amazing shoals as to appear in a vast body occupying the whole width of the river'. A local farmer used them to manure his land. A man employed to catch them used to earn four shillings a day at the rate of a halfpenny a bushel. This would represent the incredible amount of about half a million sticklebacks a day.

Armoured or not

The variation in the bony plates or scutes along the flanks has led to four types being named. There is the 'trachura' type, with a complete row of scutes from head to tail, found in the north of the range and in salty waters and usually in half-grown individuals only. In the same areas live the 'semi-armata' type with scutes halfway along the body. In fresh waters in England and France are the 'gymnura' type with 3 or 4 scutes behind the head, and the 'hologymnura' form, without scutes, found in the south of the range.

Mixed carnivorous diet

The food of sticklebacks is almost any small invertebrate, the size of the prey depending on the age of the fish. It includes small crustaceans such as water fleas and freshwater shrimps, worms, small molluscs and their larvae, aquatic insects and their larvae, and sometimes fish eggs. Corresponding marine invertebrates are taken by those living in salt water, and these grow more quickly and to a slightly greater maximum size than those living in freshwater.

Nest-building fishes

As the breeding season approaches the male becomes more brightly coloured, with red on the front part of the underside. He is then called a red throat. He takes over a territory and drives out other intruding sticklebacks. In the centre of the territory he

▽ *Breeding preliminaries: a male three-spined stickleback building his nest. The nest is held together by a secretion from a modified part of his kidney.*

builds a nest of small pieces of plants glued together with a sticky secretion from his kidneys. In the sea sticklebacks use pieces of the smaller seaweeds. The nest is lodged among the stems of water plants—among seaweeds in the sea—and when ready the male entices one or more females to lay her eggs in it. As each female lays and then departs the male enters the nest and sheds his milt to fertilise the eggs, which are just under $\frac{1}{12}$ in. diameter. These hatch in 5—12 days, according to the temperature, and during this time the male aerates them by fanning water through the nest. The 4-spined stickleback makes a nest with two holes in the top and the male puts his mouth against one hole and sucks water through the nest. The baby sticklebacks, $\frac{1}{6}$ in. long when hatched, are guarded by the male until they are ready to leave the nest. They grow to 1—2 in. long in the first year. The life span in the wild is $3\frac{1}{2}$ years.

Enemies

In spite of their armatures of spines sticklebacks are eaten, more especially by kingfishers and grebes. They tend to be infected with tapeworm, but this varies with the locality. In some lakes they are all infected.

Study in courtship

The 3-spined stickleback became more than a sport for young anglers when Niko Tinbergen did his now famous study on its courtship. It provides a simple illustration, among other things, of the use by animals of sign stimuli. A male stickleback guarding his territory attacks another male because it has a red 'throat'. Even a wooden model held in a stickleback's territory will be attacked, provided it has a red throat. A female, ready to lay, on entering the territory, turns her abdomen swollen with ripe eggs towards him as he approaches. On seeing this he swims excitedly in what is called a zigzag dance. He will respond in the same way to a wooden model having the same shape. Having danced to her, the male turns and swims towards the nest. She follows and enters it after the male has indicated its position by pointing his head at the entrance. She enters and he butts her in the flank with his snout and trembles, which makes her respond by laying. He then enters the nest after she has left it and fertilises the eggs. The spawning is the result of a series of orderly stereotyped actions, each successive step being touched off by a definite signal or sign-stimulus, the red throat, swollen abdomen, zigzag dance and so on. It is, however, not so stereotyped that it never varies. For example if the female is more than ready to lay she may make straight for the nest.

▽ *A fifteen-spined stickleback: the slender* **Spinachia spinachia** *only lives in saltwater.*

class	**Pisces**
order	**Gasterosteiformes**
family	**Gasterosteidae**
genus & species	*Gasterosteus aculeatus* 3-spined stickleback, others

▽ *Not as dangerous as it looks: a male three-spined stickleback keeps a watchful eye on his young.*

Stick-nest rat

Stick-nest rats rival the packrats (p 1668) of America in the large nests of sticks they build. Early colonists in Australia called them 'native rats' or 'rabbit-rats' because their relatively large ears and blunt noses gave them somewhat the appearance of small rabbits sitting hunched up. Stick-nest rats vary in length from $5\frac{1}{2}-8$ in. and the long hairy tail, slightly tufted at the tip, may be as much as $9\frac{3}{4}$ in. long in **Leporillus apicalis**. The fur is thick and downy, the upperparts varying from light yellowish and dull brown to pale grey-brown, with grey or white underparts.

There are three species of stick-nest rat. **L. conditor** and **L. apicalis** live in south-central Australia and **L. jonesi** on Franklin Island off the coast of South Australia. **L. jonesi** is distinguished by having shorter ears and not such thick fur which is coloured dark amber-brown on the back. **L. apicalis** has a slighter build, a paler greyish-brown back, white fur underneath and a white-tipped tail. The mainland species were once abundant but are now confined to a few areas, remote from human habitation. The island species, however, is more flourishing and has a much better chance of survival than those on the mainland.

Stronghold against predators

The stick-nest rats are unusual for their habit of building nests of sticks for shelter and breeding. Some of these are communal and house large colonies. The nests vary in size and structure to suit the local conditions. Those of *L. conditor* are usually constructed around a bush and the sticks are strongly interwoven among the stems and branches of the bush. The nests are built up to a height of about 3 ft and are up to 4 ft in diameter, sometimes larger. They are constructed with great care and form a stronghold against the dingo, and carnivorous marsupials and also against high winds. In the centre of the larger nests are several soft grass nests with numerous entrances and passages leading to them. In areas where the bushes are too small or weak to be used for supports, the nests are just loose heaps of sticks placed over rabbit warrens, the tunnels of which give the animals easy means of escape. Moreover, stones are worked into these unsupported nests and other stones are placed on top, as in Swiss chalets. The stones weigh the nests down, anchoring them against high winds.

On Franklin Island, *L. jonesi* sometimes builds enormous nests of sticks and debris on the top of the cliffs, housing extra large colonies of rats. One such nest was built on the abandoned nest of a sea eagle as a foundation. The larger nests are sometimes on top of penguin burrows and it has been observed that on the approach of danger, penguins, mutton-birds, bandicoots, and even black tiger snakes, will bolt into the burrows and tunnels with the rats.

On the shore or the flatter parts of the island the nests are small, housing usually only one pair of rats and made only of dried herbage or seaweed. In small nests there is only one chamber and one or two entrance tunnels; on the shore the nest may be no more than dried seaweed tucked between large stones.

Very little is known of the habits of *L. apicalis* except from reports of it dated 1864, but it seems it does not consistently build nests. Sometimes it will shelter in hollow trees or the deserted nests of *L. conditor*. It is gregarious like the other two species and also nocturnal.

Stick-nest rats can be easily tamed and make gentle pets.

Mainly vegetarian

They are largely vegetarian. *L. jonesi* on Franklin Island feeds mainly on the leaves of a plant *Tetragona*. There is, however, the suspicion that they may sometimes eat the eggs and young of birds. For example, there is the record of the nest of a striped brown hawk being built on top of a nest of *L. conditor*. Although the hawk did not molest the rats there were signs that the rats raided the nest when it was left unguarded.

Breeding

Little is known of the breeding habits of stick-nest rats except that the young are born in the soft grass nests in the centre of the stick nests. The female has four teats so probably, unlike most rodents, she has a fairly small litter. The young of *L. jonesi* are carried about by the mother, hanging from her teats which they grasp firmly in their mouths, a habit which originally gave rise to the mistaken idea that the rat was a pouchless marsupial. This habit, however, is seen in a number of small rodents in different parts of the world.

Cave owl an enemy

Dingos find it hard to penetrate the stick-nest shelters, so the chief enemy of the rats seems to be the cave owl. It preys especially on *L. conditor* on the desolate Nullarbor Plain where the owl lives in the numerous limestone caves. In the past the Aborigines hunted the rats for their flesh and in settled parts of New South Wales *L. apicalis* is thought to have been exterminated by introduced foxes and domestic cats.

Early observations

The stick-nests of *L. conditor* were first observed by Surveyor-General Mitchell on his expedition into the interior of eastern Australia in 1838. When Mitchell's party first saw the numerous piles of sticks on the plains of the Murray and Lower Darling in New South Wales, they naturally thought they were piles of brushwood put there by Aborigines for their signal fires. They had no reason to suspect rats because this as a rodents' habit was then unknown. Closer examination of these carefully-constructed nests and the fact that the kangaroo dogs scratched and barked at them, made Mitchell and his party curious, and on breaking open a nest—with the utmost difficulty—they found the soft nests inside containing small animals which 'might readily pass for a small rabbit but for the tail'. Unfortunately Mitchell did not keep careful watch on any animal in the nest and reported that the nests were made by the white-footed rabbit-rat, *Conilurus albipes*, a rodent common then in New South Wales and Victoria, and a relative of the stick-nest rats.

It was not until 1844 when Captain Sturt led an expedition into central Australia that it was realised the animal was a distinct species and it was given the specific name of *conditor* meaning a maker or contriver. Sturt brought back a specimen of the rat and in his narrative of the expedition dated 1849 he gives a full account of the animal and its unusual nest-building habits, illustrated by drawings.

Leporillus conditor is more rat-like than the other two species, although, but for the tail, it could be mistaken for a small rabbit.

John Norris Wood

class	**Mammalia**
order	**Rodentia**
family	**Muridae**
genus & species	*Leporillus conditor* *L. apicalis* *L. jonesi*

Stifftail

Stifftails are a group of ducks which have their tails made up of stiff feathers. They are small ducks, 14–18 in. long, and have a characteristic short, thick neck which can be inflated by an airsac under the oesophagus. The bill is broad, the wings short and the feet large. The plumage is often finely spotted and barred, with the underparts white mottled with brown, but no metallic sheens as are found in other ducks. Stifftails are found in most parts of the world but the majority of them are poorly known.

Among the better known stifftails is the ruddy duck of America and the white-headed duck of Eurasia. The ruddy duck ranges from northern Canada to Tierra del Fuego, being found over most of North and Central America and the West Indies, but is restricted to the region of the Andes in South America. In its breeding plumage the male is chestnut above, mottled white and brown underneath. The head is black except for white cheeks. The South American population is divided into two subspecies the Peruvian ruddy duck which lacks white cheeks and the Colombian in which they are mottled. The white-headed duck that breeds in parts of Europe, Asia and North Africa is similar to the ruddy duck but is less chestnut above. The maccoa duck of southern and eastern Africa and the blue-billed duck of Australia are like the ruddy duck but lack the white cheeks. Other stifftails include the white-backed duck of Africa, the musk duck of Australia with a strange lobe under the bill, and the black-headed duck of South America.

Grebe-like ducks

Stifftails are usually found on freshwater, preferring ponds and marshes where there is plenty of food. They are good divers, resembling grebes in their behaviour and associate with them rather than with other ducks. If alarmed, they can slowly submerge until only the head is showing, then disappear without a ripple. Their progress on land also recalls grebes and divers. They cannot walk properly because their legs are placed well back so they shuffle along on their bellies. The dependence of stifftails on water is further shown by the difficulty of introducing them to collections; they suffer on long journeys from not being able to swim. Although stifftails find difficulty in take-off they fly well and some species migrate. Their flight is heavy because their wings are small compared with their heavy bodies.

Varied diet

The food of stifftails is aquatic plants and animals. The white-headed duck eats mainly leaves and seeds, and also fly larvae, snails and crustaceans. The masked duck eats mainly weeds and the musk duck is most unusual in that it has a carnivorous diet and will even attack smaller ducks.

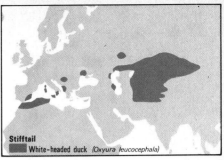

Philippa Scott

◁ *Foaming at the bows a ruddy duck, as part of his courtship display, coyly flicks his tail up over his back and presses his bill into his puffed-up breast. This North American ruddy duck is characterised by its white cheeks.*
▽ *A male white-headed duck in breeding plumage. The stifftails are a group of extremely aquatic freshwater ducks. Their stiff tails probably serve an important underwater function when they dive for food or quietly submerge, disappearing from view with hardly a ripple.*

Philippa Scott

Helpful males

Because they nest in thick reed beds in inaccessible places the breeding habits of some stifftails are poorly known. In general, the nests are elaborate and well hidden. The eggs are very large, sometimes as big as those of ducks three times their size. The male helps care for the family, although he does not help to incubate.

The courtship behaviour of male stifftails with their bright plumage is quite spectacular. They inflate their throat sacs so they look like pouter pigeons and tilt their tails over their backs, repeatedly pressing the bill into the inflated breast and clucking or squeaking. The male Argentinian ruddy duck has been described as bringing its bill down on its inflated chest with such force that it produces a drumming sound audible up to about 50 yd away.

The nest is built among sedges, reeds or bulrushes which are arched over the nest for better concealment. The white-headed duck sometimes builds floating nests but more often the nest is firmly woven into standing plants. The white-headed duck and the blue-billed duck sometimes take over the abandoned nests of coots, grebes and other ducks.

The ruddy duck lays up to 14 eggs which together may weigh 3 lb, the equivalent of three times the weight of the duck that laid them. The usual clutch is smaller but up to 20 have been found in one nest. The chicks hatch in 3 weeks and shortly after they are escorted to the water by both parents. They can dive for food almost immediately.

Strange ducks

The Australian musk duck is peculiar on account of the pouch under the bill, which is larger in males than in females, and of the musk gland which secretes an unpleasant odour in the breeding season. Not surprisingly, musk ducks are not good to eat, although this is probably due to their largely carnivorous diet; the ruddy duck feeds mainly on plants and is good to eat. The musk duck also kills other water birds, attacking them from under the water.

Another species with unusual habits is the black-headed duck. It is not very closely related to the other stifftails. It is probably an aquatic cuckoo because its nest has never been found but eggs that are very likely to be those of the black-headed duck have been found in the nests of other birds, even in those of caracaras.

class	**Aves**
order	**Anseriformes**
family	**Anatidae**
genera & species	*Biziura lobata* musk duck *Heteronetta atricapilla* black-headed duck *Oxyura australis* blue-billed duck *O. jamaicensis* ruddy duck *O. leucocephala* white-headed duck *O. maccoa* maccoa duck *Thalassornis leuconotus* white-backed duck

2219

Stilt

The stilts belong to the same family of waders as the avocet (p 107) and the ibisbill. While the bill of the avocet is turned up at the tip and that of the ibisbill turned down, those of the stilts are straight. Stilts have proportionately longer legs than any other waders and the head and body length is about 15 in. The stilt **Himantopus himantopus** is black and white and has a very large range and a variety of common names to describe its different races. The black-winged stilt breeds in Africa, southern Europe and Asia, from the Mediterranean Sea to China and occasionally in the Low Countries. There are only two records of breeding in Britain, both in 1945. The American race, called the black-necked stilt, has a continuous black band from the crown to the back. It breeds from the southern United States to northern South America, including the Galapagos Islands and the West Indies. In Australia and New Zealand the local race is called the white-headed or pied stilt. In parts of New Zealand there is a black stilt, which is probably no more than a black variety of the pied stilt.

The second species is the banded stilt which is found only in Australia. It is black and white with a chestnut band across the breast. The related ibisbill **Ibidorhyncha struthersii** lives in the high country of Central Asia.

Useful long legs

Stilts live in pairs or small flocks around shallow lakes, slow rivers, marshes and flooded agricultural land, preferring shallow water where there is plenty of water weed and low plants but not water overgrown with reeds. The banded stilt lives near temporary salt lakes and occasionally it is seen in estuaries, but it appears to shun freshwater. Stilts walk with a slow, graceful gait picking up their slender pink legs and placing them delicately, in long strides. In flight, stilts have a rapid wingbeat and they carry their heads held in. On long flights they trail their legs behind the tail making an unmistakable silhouette. On short flights and when they are manoeuvring, stilts use their long legs as a rudder.

Picking and probing

Most of the stilts' food is picked up from water plants or from the surface of the water but they also probe in the mud as they wade in shallow water up to their 'knees', and occasionally up to their bellies. This simple feeding behaviour is reflected in the unspecialised straight bill, which contrasts with the avocet's upturned bill, used for sweeping the mud and the ibisbill's downturned bill, used for probing under stones.

Stilts eat a wide variety of food; mainly insects such as water beetles, fly pupae and larvae taken from the water and caterpillars picked off leaves, as well as worms, snails and tadpoles. Banded stilts depend mainly on crustaceans from salt lakes.

Weber/Hafner: WWF

*◁ Tilted stilt in a salt marsh: a black-winged stilt searches for insects among plants of **Salicornia**. It also feeds in water, its extra long legs enabling it to feed in deeper water than most other waders.*

▷ Its long, thin legs stretched out behind it, a black-winged stilt rises skywards.

▽ A family profile: adaptive radiation of bills in the Recurvirostridae, associated with different methods of feeding. The avocet's bill is the only one that befits the family name; it is swept from side to side to catch small invertebrates. The straight bill of the stilt is the least specialised—used to pick food off water plants or gently probe in the mud. The bill of the ibisbill is a more efficient probe for getting food from under stones.

▽▽ A baby black-winged stilt paddles awkwardly along with its oversize legs.

Vaucher: WWF

Nesting hazards

Stilts nest in colonies near their feeding grounds, and sometimes the nests are built in shallow water. They may be no more than scantily lined hollows especially if in a tussock of grass or they may be substantial structures of plants and mud. The clutch is usually of 4, sometimes 3, eggs which are incubated by both parents. The chicks hatch out in 25—26 days and leave the nest soon afterwards. Their parents defend them by flying around intruders and performing distraction displays.

The nests of the banded stilt were not discovered until 1930 when a colony was discovered at Lake Grace in Western Australia. Since then other colonies have been found, some with tens of thousands of stilts, but nesting does not occur regularly at any one place. It is dependent on the rainfall in an area as this controls the availability of food and the suitability of the nesting sites.

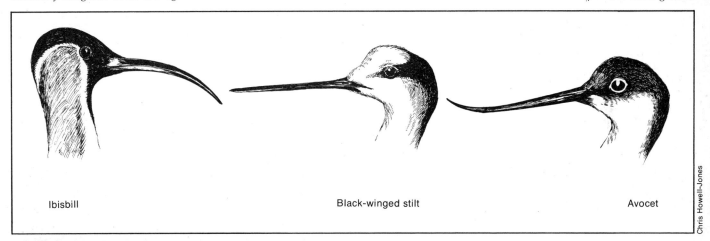

Ibisbill　　　　　　　　　Black-winged stilt　　　　　　　　　Avocet

Chris Howell-Jones

JLS Dubois: Jacana

For instance, attempts have been made to nest at Lake Grace since 1930 but they have failed through flooding.

Mixed breeding

At one time the black stilt of New Zealand was thought to form a separate species but it is now generally considered to be a black form of the pied stilt, with which it can interbreed. In recent years the pied stilt has greatly increased while the black stilt has been reduced to about 100. It has been supposed that the black form is the original New Zealand form and that the pied form is an immigrant from Australia. Why the pied stilt should be so successful, apparently at the black stilt's expense, is not known. Interbreeding produces intermediate forms which would tend to reduce the populations of black forms, but the amount of interbreeding is limited by the black stilt's preference for mating with its own kind.

class	**Aves**
order	**Charadriiformes**
family	**Recurvirostridae**
genera & species	***Cladorhynchus leucocephalus*** *banded stilt* ***Himantopus himantopus*** *black-winged stilt*

Stingray

To say stingrays sting is an under-statement: they wound with a thrust of a poison dagger. Pliny, the Roman naturalist, wrote that the spine was as strong as iron, would pierce armour like an arrow, and driven into its root would cause a tree to wither.

The stingrays, related to skates, have a flattened body with wing-like pectoral fins and a whiplike tail bearing a long poison spine. The disc-like body may have a rounded leading edge or it may be drawn out slightly into a pointed snout. The pectoral fins and the pelvics are also rounded. The surface of the body is smooth with few or no denticles. The tail is slender and at least as long as the rest of the body. The spiracles are larger than the eyes. There is no dorsal fin, and the most obvious feature is the spine set in the tail, about a third of the way along. The upper surface is usually grey or brown, sometimes with white spots or with darker marbling. The undersurface is white to creamy white. Stingrays measure from 12 in. to 14½ ft across the fins, and weigh from 1½ lb up to 750 lb.

The 100 or more species live in tropical and temperate seas, as far north in summer as southern Scandinavia in Europe and equivalent latitudes elsewhere. They all live in shallow seas, seldom going deeper than 400 ft. Some species enter estuaries and even go up rivers, in a few instances for considerable distances.

△ *Dappled danger:* **Potamotrygon***, a species from South America which never leaves freshwater.*
◁ *An unwelcome inhabitant of the Bahamas' shores:* **Dasyatis americana** *moves off.*

Rapid action poison

Stingrays, like skates, spend much of their time on the seabed, searching for prey or merely resting. They move by wave-like undulations passing along the two pectoral fins, the tail being useless for swimming. When attacked, or even if only disturbed, the ray lashes with its tail, from side to side in some species, or bringing the tail up and over the body in others. This brings the swordlike spine into play. It is up to 15 in. long in the largest of the rays, with sawtoothed edges and grooves. The grooves are lined with a glistening white tissue which probably contains the poison.

The stab from a stingray not only injects poison, but also cuts and tears the flesh, and many people that have trodden on a stingray lying in shallow water have had to have stitches in their feet. Even a tiny puncture from the spine of a stingray has made a man faint. The effect of the poison is immediate and inflammation spreads around the wound almost as soon as the spine has penetrated. Other immediate symptoms are sharp shooting pains and throbbing. The poison affects the heart, breathing and nerves and it can be fatal although there are fairly simple remedies provided they are applied quickly. At one time washing the wound with iodine or permanganate of potash was recommended. Today, the treatment is to clean the wound, then immerse it in hot water for up to an hour, and give an anti-tetanus injection.

Clam-cracker

The mouth of the stingray is on the undersurface of the head. The jaws are wide and both have blunt teeth arranged like a pavement in rows, with several rows of broad teeth in the middle and rows of smaller teeth on each side. A North American species known as the stingaree is also called the clam-cracker. Its food, like that of other stingrays, is mainly molluscs and crustaceans, and sometimes fish.

Born alive

All stingrays are ovoviviparous. That is, the eggs are not laid but hatch in the oviduct, the young being eventually born alive. At first the young feed on the yolk in a yolk-sac hanging from their abdomens, the food passing direct into the digestive tube from the yolk-sac. Then, at a later stage, blood vessels grow out and around the yolk, and food is taken into the blood. Later tiny filaments grow out from the walls of the oviduct. Each has a network of tiny blood vessels and gives out a liquid food which the embryo stingray takes through its mouth or through its spiracles. It is the equivalent of the placenta in mammals.

Bayonet teeth

Rays and sharks do not have scales like bony fishes. Their skin is protected by dermal denticles (or 'little teeth in the skin'). Each denticle is made up of a pulp cavity inside a layer of dentine with a kind of enamel on the outside. These were once thought to be the equivalent of real teeth but with further biochemical research it is now realized they are not. For example, the 'dentine' is not true dentine. It has not yet been decided whether the spine of a stingray is a modified, and greatly enlarged, dermal denticle or not. One thing it shares with true teeth is that the spine may be replaced by a new one. Should the old spine not drop out before the new one grows out, the stingray may temporarily have two spines with which to lash its enemies, and exceptionally it may have three or four. These niceties would have held no interest for the peoples of the South Pacific who used them for spearheads. One of the dangers of being wounded by a stingray is that the poison tissue in its grooves may be left behind in the wound. Even worse, the spine may snap off and the piece left in the wound is very painful to remove. It is the equivalent of the saw-edged bayonet that was banned years ago.

class	**Selachii**
order	**Hypotremata**
family	**Dasyatidae**
genus & species	*Dasyatis pastinaca* *others*

2223

Stoat

The stoat, a relative of the larger polecat (p. 1811), is up to 17 in. or more in length including 4½ in. of long-haired tail. The males are larger than the females, weighing from 7 oz to 1 lb, while the females weigh only 5–10 oz. The fur is reddish-brown with the white underparts and throat tinged with yellow. The tail is the same colour as the back except for the tuft of long black hairs on the tip. Like the polecat, the stoat can secrete an objectionable odour from its scent glands, but this is not quite so offensive as in the larger animal.

In winter in the northern parts of its range the stoat's fur becomes white all over, with the exception of the tip of the tail which always remains black. It is then known as ermine and is valuable to the fur-trade. In Great Britain the traditional ceremonial robes of royalty and nobility have always been made from ermine.

The stoat is widespread in Europe from the Alps and Pyrenees to the Arctic shores and east into Asia. It is also found in North America where it is known as the short-tailed weasel. The stoat is found throughout the British Isles and a smaller local race, varying somewhat in colour, is found in Ireland where it is known as the weasel. Another local race, the Islay stoat, is found on the Isle of Jura on the west coast of Scotland.

Snake-like hunter

The stoat is found in most types of country, hunting along hedgerows, across fields, by rivers and brooks or wherever there is a chance of food. It moves characteristically in a succession of low bounds, its long, lithe body assuming an almost snake-like appearance. It can swim and climb well. Its senses of smell and hearing are acute but its sight is poor. Whether hunting or not, the stoat is alert, agile and energetic, with a natural ability to take advantage of cover. A common trick is to use the runs of moles or rats, either to escape enemies or to hunt prey. There are a number of accounts of stoats playing together, twisting and turning like snakes, zigzagging over the ground, rolling over each other, somersaulting on the ground or in mid-air, leaping anything up to four feet into the air and, finally, sitting up on their hind-legs and boxing furiously with their fore-paws.

Although largely nocturnal in its habits, there is a good chance of seeing a stoat hunting in broad daylight.

Truly carnivorous

A stoat hunts largely by scent, picking up the trail of its prey and following this relentlessly. Truly carnivorous, it rejects little that is flesh. Until the disease myxomatosis reduced the numbers of rabbits in Europe, they formed the stoat's main food. A rabbit will cry out in terror, apparently paralysed with fear, even while the stoat is some way off. Similarly, a hare, which can outwit a

△ As a tribute to her spotless virginity, the artist portrays Queen Elizabeth I with a pure white ermine.
◁ Ermine not stoat. Except for the black tip on its tail, which always remains black, this stoat has moulted to its winter coat, having discarded its brown summer coat in a matter of days.

fox or a pack of trained hounds, becomes so terrorised that it hardly tries to escape.

Given the opportunity a stoat can be destructive to game and poultry, which has led to its persecution by gamekeepers and poultry farmers from early times. The fact that it also destroys vermin is not so commonly stressed. Moles, rats, mice and voles are killed by a bite at the back of the neck. It also takes fish, small birds, eggs and reptiles. It will sometimes employ tactics known as 'charming' (see red fox p 1929).

Family parties on the hunt

Fertile matings take place in March and again in June and July and because the males are partially sexually active until October, infertile mating may take place after July. After fertilisation in the spring and summer, implantation is delayed until the following spring, after which there is a gestation period of 20–28 days. The nursery is made in a hole in a bank or the hollow of a decayed tree and in April or May 4 or 5 young are born, occasionally 6–9. The female alone tends the young, which she will defend fiercely against all dangers. She has only one litter a year. The babies are covered with fine white hair at birth, the black tip appears on the tail at

20 days and the eyes open at 27 days. Weaning is at 5 weeks of age.

The young remain with their mother after weaning and hunt with their parents in a family party. Two or more family parties may join up, like some of the larger carnivores, to form the well-known packs of stoats that are reputed to attack dogs and even men. When, through an increase in their numbers, the food supply of a district is largely reduced, the stoats sometimes migrate in large numbers. There are reports of several scores of them moving across country in a column, but these stories are viewed with caution by many zoologists. Apart from man the stoat has few enemies, but young stoats and a few adults are taken by owls and hawks.

Change in colour

It was believed for a long time that the change in the colour of the coat in autumn was caused not by the loss of hairs but by the loss of pigment in the hairs. This is now known to be incorrect. A stoat moults twice a year in spring and autumn and, as has already been said, its coat turns white in northern latitudes. The change from brown to white is very rapid because the

△ *A stoat on the look-out, its body sprung for action. It is a remarkably fast and agile animal.*
An expert hunter, it will climb trees and pursue its prey into small holes and burrows.

▷ *A first look at life: two young stoats gaze*
inquisitively at the world about them.

new white coat grows underneath the old one. The old coat may be shed in as little as three days in very cold conditions.

The accepted idea is that the summer russet coat is protective in that it harmonises generally with the colour of the leaf litter over which the stoat is moving, and that on snow-covered ground, as in Alpine districts, the change to a white fur enables the stoat to steal up on its prey unseen. It is not easy, however, to accept this when we recall the behaviour of rabbits and hares in the presence of a stoat. Their

terror must almost certainly be induced by the sight of the animal. Even if it were induced by smell, it would still suggest that any coat colour is not of primary value as camouflage. More likely, a white coat cuts down the loss of body heat, as in the plumage of the ptarmigan (p 1854).

Although the matter has not been fully investigated, experiments have shown that the change in colour of the stoat's coat seems to be dependent partly upon temperature and partly upon day length. Since both these factors are variable many permutations can

result. In North America, for instance, all stoats turn white in the north, and in the south all remain russet, but there is a zone between where white, particoloured or russet stoats are found in winter. Again, in the south of England, an occasional stoat will turn white in the autumn, whereas others may be partly white and partly coloured. Both these forms may occur in a mild winter when there is little or no snow. One explanation for this is that temperature may also have a delayed action, so that a stoat experiencing lowered temperatures in one autumn may turn white in the following autumn even if temperatures are high. But the fact that white or partly white stoats in southern England tend to be localised suggests that the change is genetic.

Stoat (*Mustela erminea*)

class	**Mammalia**
order	**Carnivora**
family	**Mustelidae**
genus & species	*Mustela erminea* stoat, ermine or short-tailed weasel *M. e. hibernica* Irish weasel *M. e. ricinae* Islay stoat

Eric Hosking

Stone curlew

The stone curlews or thickknees are strange-looking waders, the nine species making up the family Burhinidae. The former name is due to their preference for pebbly ground and the latter to the swollen 'knee' joints. They range in size from 14–21 in. long. The legs are fairly long, the feet slightly webbed and the hindtoe is missing. The bill is usually short and thick, yellow or green with a black tip, and the eyes are large. The plumage is dull grey with streaks of brown and black.

The European stone curlew, about 16 in. long, has sandy-brown plumage with black streaks and white wing bars. The bill is short and straight. It lives in Europe, including the British Isles, from Poland and Germany south to the Mediterranean, in Africa south to Kenya and in southern Asia. Other stone curlews include the water thickknee of South Africa and the bush curlew and beach curlew of Australia. The beach curlew is 21 in. long and has a massive bill which is slightly flattened and upturned. Other stone curlews are found in tropical and temperate regions, including South America, but are missing entirely from North America, the islands of the Pacific and New Zealand.

Waders far from water

Although they are waders, most stone curlews are found well away from water, often in dry upland regions or in sandy country. The bush curlew is found in light wooded and open country; the double-striped thick-knee is found in the savannahs of Central and South America and the South American thickknee is found in the sandy deserts of Peru and Ecuador. As the lack of a hind toe suggests, they are strong runners and there is some indication that they are more closely related to bustards than curlews. When the bush curlew, for instance, is chased it seeks safety by running, and if it does take to the air it has to taxi to take off. Then it lands quickly and runs into cover.

Stone curlews are nocturnal, as is suggested by their large eyes, the pupils of which contract considerably during the day. At night the stone curlews are very noisy, producing cries which are often mournful, rather like those of curlews. During the day they are quiet and lie up in cover. When disturbed they flatten themselves with their head and neck extended; so with their drab plumage they are very difficult to find.

Mainly insect diet

Stone curlews feed on insects, such as beetles, grasshoppers and fly maggots, and on snails, slugs and worms. Those that live near water also feed on crustaceans. Small rodents, chicks of game birds, amphibians and reptiles are also eaten.

Pre-fab nests

At the start of the breeding season male stone curlews display vigorously, running about with outstretched wings. No nest is made and the two eggs, one in the beach curlew, are laid in a bare scrape. The water dikkop sometimes lays its eggs on the dried droppings of elephants or hippopotamus. At the start of incubation the parent stone curlew quietly creeps away from the nest when disturbed, but later it sits tight. Both parents incubate the eggs, which hatch in 25–27 days. The chicks leave the scrape shortly after hatching.

△ *Proud parents with their chick, the stone curlew **Burhinus oedicnemus**. The nest is just a depression scraped in the bare ground.*

Watch dog for crocs

The water dikkop is one of the so-called crocodile birds (see courser p 540). There seems to be no evidence that the water dikkop takes food from a crocodile's mouth, as crocodile birds are traditionally supposed to do, but it does associate with crocodiles during the nesting season. Both animals breed on sand banks when the rivers are low and water dikkops can be found sitting on their eggs only a few feet from a crocodile guarding its own nest. They are probably safe because when not actually hunting, the crocodiles are not concerned with food. The birds may even gain protection from nest predators by the crocodiles' proximity. The crocodile is in return given warning of enemies by the water dikkop's alarm calls. Hippopotamus also heed the water dikkop's warnings and in South America double-striped thickknees are hand reared by the local peoples to act as watch dogs.

class	**Aves**
order	**Charadriiformes**
family	**Burhinidae**
genera & species	***Burhinus vermiculatus*** *water dikkop* ***B. bistriatus*** *double-striped thickknee* ***B. superciliaris*** *South American thickknee* ***B. magnirostris*** *bush curlew* ***B. oedicnemus*** *European stone curlew* ***Orthorhamphus magnirostris*** *beach curlew, others*

Stonefish

The stonefish is almost the ugliest, if not the ugliest of all fishes and it is certainly the most poisonous. A stonefish is 6—12 in. long, has a heavy head which is broad and flat, and the body tapers rapidly from behind the head to the small tailfin. The mouth is wide and has a fairly large gape. The pectoral fins are large and winglike. The dorsal fin, which runs along the midline of the back, is armed with 13 stout spines. There are three more spines on the anal fin and one on each of the pelvic fins. The scaleless skin is covered with many irregular warts and a layer of slime. The colour of the fish is best described as the colour of mud, seaweed or stone—and if stones vary in colour, so do stonefishes! One stonefish even looks like a piece of rock covered with small algae.

The three species of the world's most venomous fish are found from the Red Sea to East Africa and across the Indian Ocean to the northern coasts of Western Australia and Queensland.

Hilmar Hansen

Defences on all sides

Stonefishes live in shallow seas, especially where the bottom is coral rock or tidal mud flats. They lie completely still even when anyone goes near them and their only reaction to a foot placed a few inches from them is to erect their spines. The stonefish is virtually invisible against its background and those who are poisoned by it probably never see it. Each of the spines has two poison sacs near its tip. Pressure on this tip makes a sheath covering it slide back leaving the point of the spine bare and exposing the grooves down which the poison flows. Although normally it is the spines on the back that do the damage, if the fish is kicked so that it rolls onto its side, the stonefish can still defend itself—with the anal and pelvic fins.

Fishermen in the Indian Ocean handle stonefishes with great care, especially as the fishes can stay alive 10 hours after they have been taken out of water. Even dead specimens lying high and dry on the beach are still able to inflict a poison wound.

Waiting for food

Stonefishes wait for their food to come to them. Any passing animal not too large to be swallowed is snapped up. They do not seem to be able to see the stonefish, which consequently never lacks a meal. The fish are snapped up in its capacious mouth faster than the eye can see. One moment a fish is swimming towards the stonefish's mouth, the next moment it has vanished, and so far as the human eye can tell, nothing has moved. The poison spines are never used for catching food, but are only used in self-defence.

It is hardly surprising, with so dangerous a fish that little is known about how it breeds. Something, however, is known about its enemies—and surprisingly it has enemies. Certain bottom-feeding sharks and rays,

with crushing teeth used for eating crabs and hard-shelled molluscs, occasionally take stonefishes. There is another disadvantage in staying very still on the sea-bed. In tropical seas there are large sea-snails known as conchs which are both aggressive and carnivorous and stonefishes, especially young ones, fall victim to these.

Thirteen deadly spines

Reports on the effect of the spines on human beings differ. Some suggest that people have trodden on or handled stonefish and been either unaffected or little the worse for the experience. At the other extreme are reports of fatal results. It seems that one can be very slightly pricked in the finger and provided the sheath is not broken, or the wound only shallow, no poison will be injected. It seems also that once the spines have been touched and their poison ejected they are harmless, suggesting that the poison sacs, or the sheath, or both cannot be renewed. By contrast there are authentic cases on record of immediate, extremely painful symptoms, with death following. These speak of excruciating pain with the victim screaming, half mad with agony, collapse, delirium and maniacal ravings. Death follows in about six hours, but if the wounds are not fatal the agony may last up to eight hours then slowly diminish. There has been at least one case in which the patient did not fully recover for a year. In some instances the legs swell to elephantine proportions, there may be large blisters and the skin may slough. Fingers and toes are said to turn black and drop off.

Antidotes, which must be applied quickly, include a weak solution of hydrochloric acid or formalin and permanganate of potash. At the Serum Laboratories in Melbourne, Victoria, in Australia, an anti-venin has been produced.

△ The stone mask of a stonefish **Synanceja horrida**. One of the ugliest and most poisonous fishes, it has been little studied.
▷ Overleaf: Looking like just another stone on the sea-bed **S. verrucosa** lies in wait, its mouth and eye hardly visible against its cryptically coloured skin. Just visible along its back, 13 spines lie ready to snag an intruder.

Fatality re-enacted

Any suspicion that reports of such grievous symptoms are exaggerated can be set aside in view of the ritual performed by some of the Australian aborigines. It takes the form of a charade, which has been described by Kelvin CB Green, of Australia, and it has been enacted since the time of the Bronze Age in Europe, that is, back in the aborigines' dream-time, their equivalent of times long past. A dancer imitates a man paddling in the tidal pools looking for fishes. He takes short steps, looking to the left, to the right. Then he takes big steps and suddenly lifts one foot, grabs it with a hand, screams and limps away. He sits down, then he lies down, he writhes and screams, while a witch doctor dances around him uttering incantations. Finally, the witch doctor throws up his hands in despair and the 'patient' wails a death song. The interesting feature of this theatrical display is that the dancer carries a clay model of a fish with 13 splinters of wood stuck into its back to represent spines.

class	**Pisces**
order	**Scorpaeniformes**
family	**Scorpaenidae**
genus & species	*Synanceja horrida* *S. trachynis* *S. verrucosa*

H Hansen

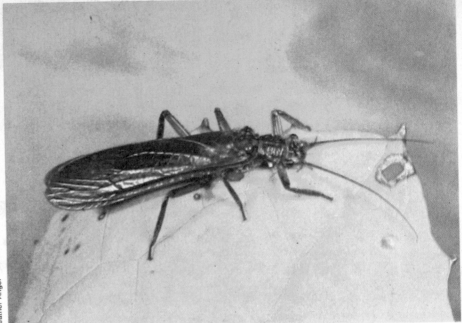

Heather Angel

SG Giacomelli

*Leaving its watery past behind, a **Perlodes micro-cephala** nymph before its final moult (× 1½).*

*A resting stonefly **Dinocras cephalotes**. The forewings are folded round each other on top of the larger hindwings. The stonefly leads a short, inactive life near water where it lays its eggs (× 3½).*

Stonefly

Stoneflies are little-known insects except to entomologists, and to anglers who use them, or imitations of them, for bait. Artificial stoneflies were first used for fishing in the 15th century. Stoneflies belong to a primitive order of insects, the Plecoptera, which have aquatic larvae. The adults also are generally found near water. They have two pairs of membranous wings, long, thread-like antennae and a pair of segmented appendages called cerci at the hinder end of the body. The name 'cercus' is from the Greek, meaning tail, and in some insects the cerci carry organs of hearing. Stoneflies are weak fliers, and when at rest the large hindwings are folded like a fan and covered by the long, narrow forewings, one of which completely overlaps the other.

*Some of the largest stoneflies are big; the North American **Pteronarcys californica** is 3½ in. long. **Perla** and **Nemoura** are the commonest European genera. Dark brown and dull green are the most usual colours, but some of the Australian species are very handsome, with rich red hindwings tinged with purple streaks. One species is jet black with orange on the front of the body.*

The larvae are basically like the adults in structure, except that they lack wings, and they have tufts of filamentous gills along each side of the body. Their legs are often fringed with hairs for swimming.

The Plecoptera, a small order of which only 1 500 species are known, is one of the most ancient insect orders; fossil stoneflies are known from the Permian period, about 250 million years ago.

Under stones at all times

Adult stoneflies are usually found resting on or under stones or on tree trunks near streams. They usually run rather than fly when disturbed. The larvae or nymphs also spend much of their time under stones on the river bed. They have weakly developed biting mouthparts and are said to feed on algae, although probably the adults of many species do not feed at all but only drink. The larvae eat plant food, such as small algae off stones, but larger species also eat the aquatic larvae of other insects.

Aerial egg-laying

The only time to see stoneflies in any numbers on or over water is when the females are laying their eggs. They do this in one of two ways. In some species the female swims on the surface dropping her eggs as she does so. The female of one large species is a strong swimmer and leaves a V-shaped wake behind her. Other females fly over water dipping the tip of the abdomen into the water every now and then; and there is a third group that fly over water alighting from time to time, just to lay eggs and then taking to the wing once more, or they may suddenly fall on the surface with their wings upstretched, releasing their eggs as soon as the abdomen touches the water.

Long larval life

The eggs are dropped into the water in thin membranous packets. The whole pre-adult life is passed in running water, which must be pure and well oxygenated because the larvae depend entirely on their gills for respiration. Larvae of some of the commonest species can easily be found by turning over stones; they live clinging to the undersides. The aquatic pre-adult life lasts at least a year, and sometimes as much as 4 years are passed in the water. During growth the wings gradually develop and there are many moults or ecdyses; up to 33

have been recorded. The larvae remain active at very low temperatures, down to almost freezing in some of the Arctic species. When the larva is ready to moult for the last time it crawls several feet from the water onto a stone or a tree, anchors itself with its hooked feet and splits down the back, releasing the winged adult insect, which takes quite a time to pull itself free.

Profit and loss

Stonefly larvae, also known as creepers by anglers, are of great importance as a source of food for trout and other fish which live in the clean swift streams that they inhabit. Some anglers maintain, however, that they are a mixed blessing because the larger of them feed on the insect larvae which sport fishes, such as trout, also eat. They eat especially the rapacious dragonfly nymphs which, according to Dr HBN Hynes, the stonefly larvae do not see but pounce on as soon as they touch their antennae or cerci, seizing them and worrying them as a terrier would a rat.

Stonefly larvae are also useful as indicators of pollution. Their presence means that a stream is almost or completely free from pollution; on the other hand their absence from apparently suitable waters is a warning that some degree of pollution is probably present, though it may still be far from offensive to the human senses.

phylum	**Arthropoda**
class	**Insecta**
order	**Plecoptera**
family	**Perlidae**
genus	*Perla*
family	**Nemouridae**
genus	*Nemoura* others